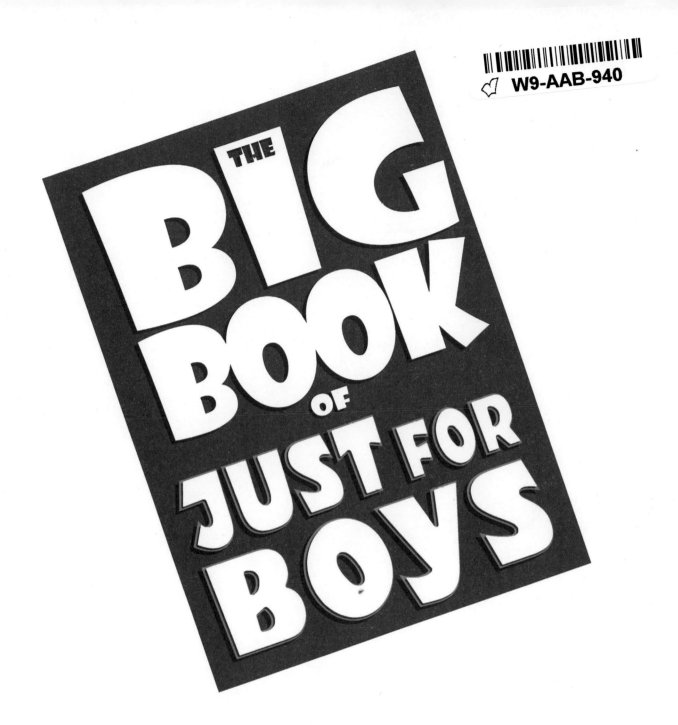

THE BIG BOOK OF JUST FOR BOYS

Kidsbooks®

Visit us at www.kidsbooks.com

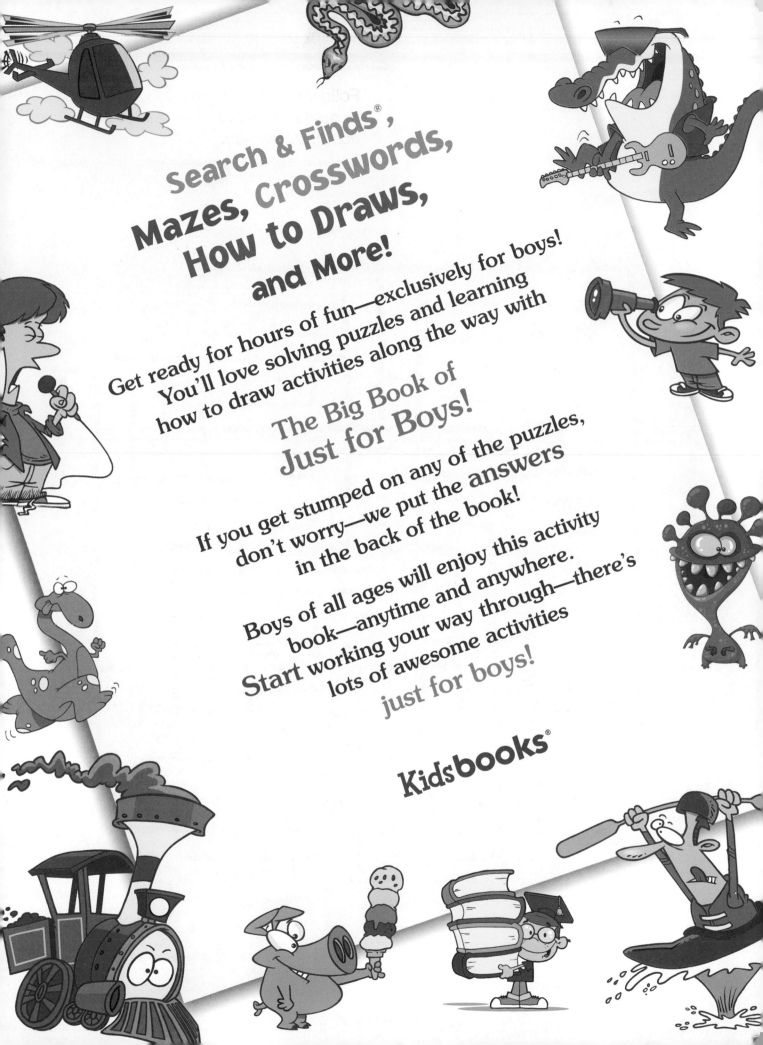

Search & Finds®, Mazes, Crosswords, How to Draws, and More!

Get ready for hours of fun—exclusively for boys! You'll love solving puzzles and learning how to draw activities along the way with

The Big Book of Just for Boys!

If you get stumped on any of the puzzles, don't worry—we put the answers in the back of the book!

Boys of all ages will enjoy this activity book—anytime and anywhere. Start working your way through—there's lots of awesome activities just for boys!

Kidsbooks®

Construction Maze

Follow the path from **Start** to **Finish** to guide the boy to the end of the construction site.

FINISH

START

Answer on page 261

Sudoku
BRAIN BUILDER

Flex those gray matter muscles and try to decode this sudoku. Fill in the empty squares so that each row, column, and square contains the numbers 1–9 only once.

		6			3		2	8
		3	4			7		
9			1			5		3
6						1	9	4
4	2	8						7
5			4		2			1
		2			7	8		
8	7			6		4		

TOOL TIME

It's time to fix stuff up! Find the names of these tools in the word search below. Look up, down, backward, forward, and diagonally.

Drill	Sander
Hammer	Saw
Level	Screwdriver
Nail gun	Trowel
Pliers	Wrench

```
S U G L R E W H L J L S P B
K C X S M A N Q C N S A J Q
N C R D R I L L R N E W N X
V N C E P Y X F E A E X I C
Q O O C W Y D U D I V R M M
E O X S G D E T N L F U W A
S R E I L P R L A G W S R L
H L W M M Y H I S U N P E Z
I C E Y X H Q D V N F W F U
S U U V A E J N O E O C B G
J C A M E S D M C R R Y F F
I N M C X L N L T G G L X F
N E C Q E M C I J J M I C G
R V O X Q K S W I S W I K I
```

Answer on page 261

Rockin' Rebus

Solve this rebus puzzle to discover the name of something fun where you'll find dribblers.

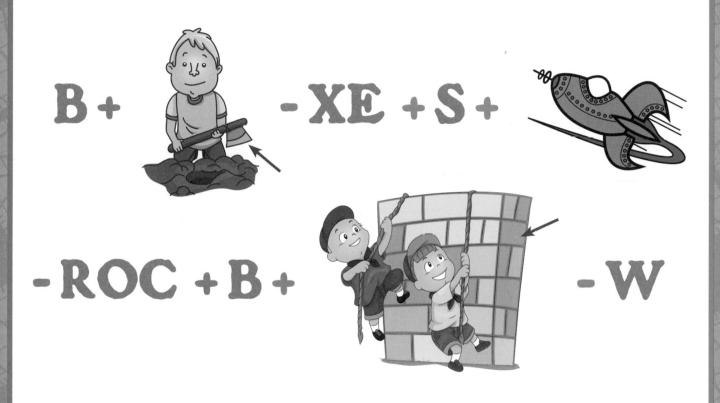

B + (man digging) - XE + S + (plane)

- ROC + B + (kids climbing wall) - W

Let's Draw a
Corvette

On a separate piece of paper, follow these simple steps using a pencil and an eraser.

1 Start by drawing the canopy, body, and tire shapes. Draw through your shapes.

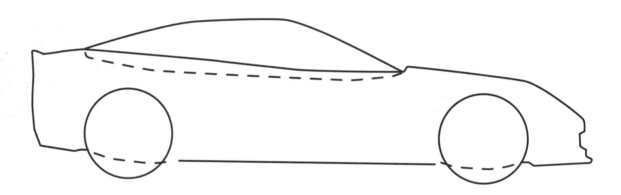

2 Erase the guidelines. Next, draw the door, wheel wells, small lights, and headlights.

3 Add rear windows, mirrors, and rims. Use lines to show the body design.

4 This Corvette looks good in purple. Add some highlights and some dark shading, a black canopy, and this car is on its way.

READY FOR THE WEEKEND

Fill in the blanks to complete this silly story about your weekend. Pick a NOUN, ADJECTIVE, or VERB from the word bank to place in a corresponding blank, or think of your own wacky words!

I can't wait for the weekend—to me it is the _____ time of the week!
[ADJECTIVE]

My favorite thing to do is _____ with my _____. My mother gets
[VERB]   [NOUN]

_____ if I _____ too much, so I try not to do that. My friends
[ADJECTIVE]   [VERB]

_____ on the weekend and I am right there with them! In the
[VERB]

blink of an eye, the weekend is over, and it's time for me to curl up in my

_____ and prep for the school week!
[NOUN]

WORD BANK

ADJECTIVES

awesome
nervous
silly
insane
magical
smart
red
straight
mushy

NOUNS

banana
ball
paper bag
t-shirt
bulldog
masterpiece
hamburger
gym shorts
jet

VERBS

sneak
pounce
jog
sleep
squat
play
borrow
drive
burp

TYPES OF ICE CREAM

Use the clues about different kinds of ice cream to solve the crossword puzzle.

ACROSS
3. Usually made with bananas
4. A mix of vanilla, chocolate, and strawberry
5. Made with ice cream, milk, and flavored syrup
7. Has a cherry on top

DOWN
1. A fruity ice cream made with only a little milk
2. A popular flavor of fruit ice cream
6. Vanilla between two cookies

Fishing
How To
TIPS

Grab your fishing pole, score some bait, and cast your reel—it's time to learn the basics of fishing. Next time you head out, you'll be a pro.

Fishing Basics

1. Pick a great location. Make sure the body of water you choose actually has FISH in it.

2. Choose your bait and hooks. Ask in your local bait shop about the size of hook you need and the type of bait, based on the type of fish you are looking to catch.

3. Cast your line and wait. If your fishing rod starts moving a lot or if you feel a pulling, odds are, you caught something. If you've been waiting for more than 20 minutes and still haven't caught anything, move on to another area.

4. Hook it. If you feel a tug on your line, jerk the line backward and up. If you have a fish, keep the line tight, pull the rod up and grab hold of the fish. Remove the hook. Do this as gently as possible.

ON THE LAKE

Find these things that have to do with boats in the word search. Look up, down, backward, forward, and diagonally.

Anchor   Ladder   Marina   Paddle   Radio

Dock   Life jacket   Outrigger   Propeller   Sail

```
O Y X G X F P J U L T E D M
F N D Q T Q M Q N G P B G P
O W J E T T S P E Z Y P R A
L A N C H O R Q R O W W K D
Q I O D X U I A K P J E P D
O I F N O N T L Z I H P A L
R U S E E C H A N Q R O I E
E Q T A J E K V C O T I K L
D F C R I A J M P X R D S W
D T V M I L C E A M V A M J
A P G I F G L K W R Z R M F
L D B N B L G S E R I D U D
O X I P E K X E G T L N N W
A L M R C H J P R Y H P A L
```

Scary Dragon

Roar! Can you find the two pictures that are exactly alike?

Answer on page 262

Big Dreams

You have to have goals, dude! List your goals here—and check them off as you get them done!

By the time I am 10, I hope to:

By the time I am 30, I hope to:

By the time I am 15, I hope to:

By the time I am 40, I hope to:

By the time I am 20, I hope to:

Are You a Sports Fanatic?

Are you a sport lover? To find out if you're a sports fanatic, read each statement, then put a check under "True" or "False." When you're done, go to the end of the quiz to see your results!

TRUE **FALSE**

1. I have more than five sports trophies in my room. ◯ ◯

2. I can calculate an ERA. ◯ ◯

3. Gym is my favorite subject. ◯ ◯

4. I prefer my football to a guitar. ◯ ◯

5. I spend more time on a field than I do anywhere else. ◯ ◯

6. I know who Michael Jordan is. ◯ ◯

7. I love wearing a uniform. ◯ ◯

8. I have been on more than five sports teams in my life.

9. I will always watch a sporting event instead of a cartoon.

10. My heroes are all athletes.

11. I spend more than five hours a week playing sports.

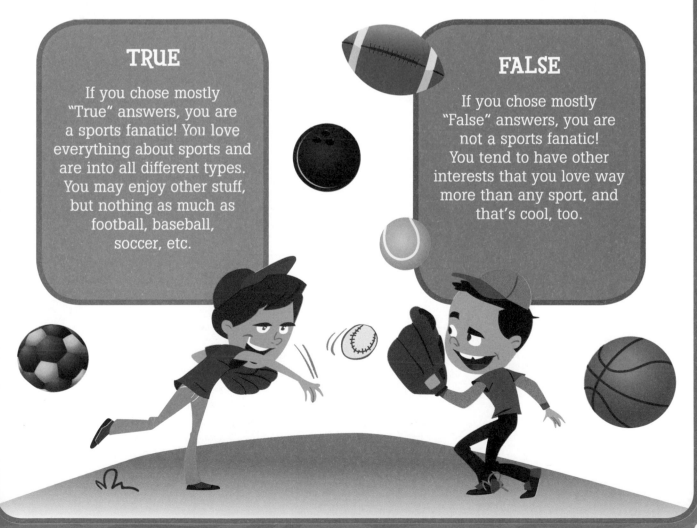

TRUE

If you chose mostly "True" answers, you are a sports fanatic! You love everything about sports and are into all different types. You may enjoy other stuff, but nothing as much as football, baseball, soccer, etc.

FALSE

If you chose mostly "False" answers, you are not a sports fanatic! You tend to have other interests that you love way more than any sport, and that's cool, too.

Sudoku
SUPER SMART

Put on your thinking cap and try to decode this sudoku. Fill in the empty squares so that each row, column, and square contains the numbers 1–9 only once.

3			5			6		
			6		9	1	3	8
				1		4	2	
			9					
9	4		1		5		8	2
					7			
	8	7		5				
5	1	6	4		8			
		9			6			1

Answer on page 262

Would You Rather...

Which would you rather do?
Look at each pair of options. Think about them and check the things you would like best. Ask your friends, too!

Would you rather every day be...

☐ Christmas   or   ☐ Halloween?

Would you rather be...

☐ A shark   or   ☐ A dinosaur?

Would you rather live...

☐ In the past   or   ☐ In the future?

Would you rather own...

☐ A toy factory   or   ☐ A car factory?

Write Your

BLOG

What was the best day you ever had so far? What made it such a memorable day? Write a blog entry about it here!

Best Day Ever!

Caption your picture _____

_____

_____

_____

_____

_____

_____

_____

_____

_____

_____

post by _____ time _____

Ready for Rebus

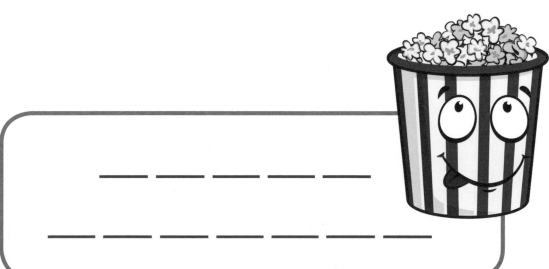

Shining Stars
FACTS

How cool is it when the night sky is clear and you can see tons and tons of stars? Here's some info on what to look for amongst the stars!

Star Bright

A constellation is a group of stars up in the sky.

Stars move around in the sky. The ONLY star that never moves is Polaris, better known as the North Star. It's located right above the North Pole. If you ever get lost, locate the North Star. Its location is always NORTH.

Little Dipper

The Little Dipper is a constellation shaped like an egg dipper or a spoon. The star at the very top of the Little Dipper is the North Star. The best way to find the North Star is to locate the Little Dipper.

Big Dipper

The Big Dipper is usually the easiest constellation to find because all the stars are really bright. It is also called "Ursa Major," which means "Big Bear" in Latin, because people used to say it looked like a bear.

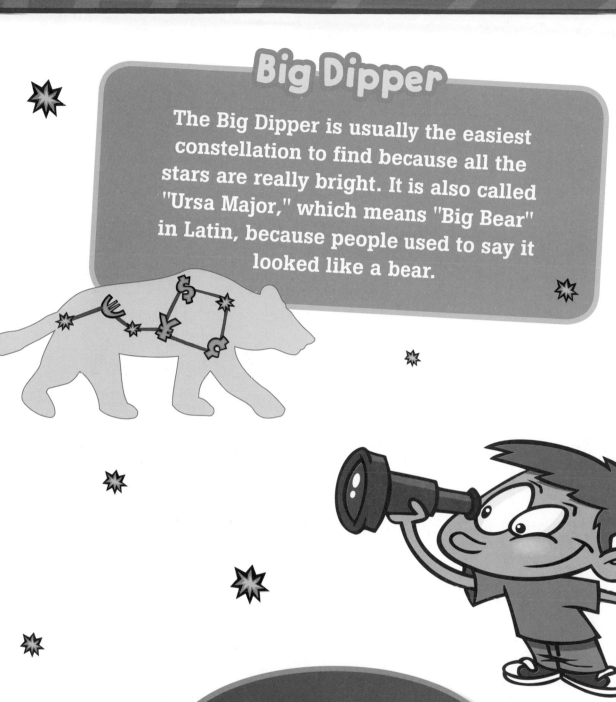

Fun Facts!

- There are hundreds of constellations. Collectively, they are referred to as the Zodiac.
- The sun is actually a star. It is the star that is closest to Earth.
- Most stars are between one and ten billion years old.

Safari Animals

Are you a super seeker? Put your eyes to the test and see if you can find 10 differences between the picture on the top and the one on the bottom.

Answer on page 263

Sundae Maze

Follow the correct path through the maze to get the man to the ice-cream sundae. What's the correct path, you ask? It's the one that is made up of bananas only!

START

FINISH

MY FIRST CAR

Fill in the blanks to complete this silly story about your future first car. Pick a NOUN, ADJECTIVE, or VERB from the word bank to place in a corresponding blank, or think of your own wacky words!

My first car is going to be a _____ and it is going to be totally
[NOUN]

_____! I'm going to _____ it every single chance I get. I'll
[ADJECTIVE]   [VERB]

definitely get the _____ model so that everyone will _____
[ADJECTIVE]   [VERB]

when they set their eyes on it. My trunk will have a _____ in it.
[NOUN]

I can't wait for the day I get my driver's license! Once I pass the driving

test, I'll be sure to _____ by all my friends in my _____ car.
[VERB]   [ADJECTIVE]

WORD BANK

ADJECTIVES

pink
shiny   enormous
muddy   crooked
little   weird
sparkly   smelly

NOUNS

lemon
tank   taxi
box   tricycle
puppy   dump
missile   sock

VERBS

rev
slide   hide
swim   sneeze
fart   steer
scream   drive

School Trip

Honk! Can you find the two pictures that are exactly alike?

Answer on page 263

Would You Rather...

Sure, you have a favorite kind of music. But, when given the choice of two types of music you may not consider too often, which would you choose? Check one in each pair!

Would you rather listen to...

☐ **Country**   or   ☐ **Classical?**

Would you rather listen to...

☐ **Hip Hop**   or   ☐ **Opera?**

Would you rather listen to...

☐ **Rock**   or   ☐ **Pop?**

Would you rather listen to...

☐ **Jazz**   or   ☐ **Techno?**

Halloween Maze

Let's party! Follow the path from **Start** to **Finish** to guide the kids to the candy.

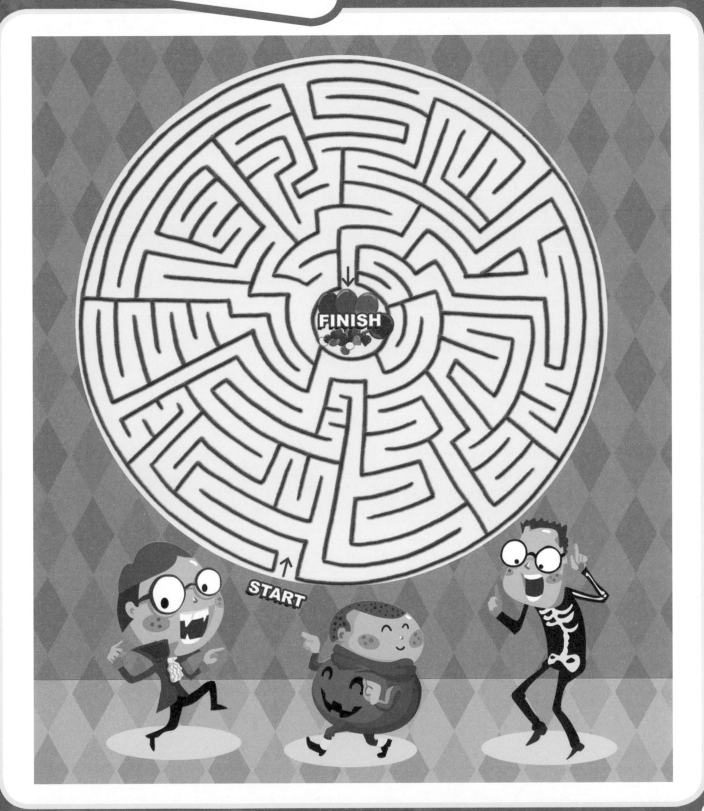

What's Your Future Career?

The future holds endless possibilities. You can do or be anything you want! Take this quiz to determine your future career.

Builder   Designer   Problem Solver

1. You're bored. What do you do?
- **A -** Gather bits and pieces of anything from around the house and build a robot.
- **B -** Grab my markers and draw the finest piece of graffiti known to man.
- **C -** Patrol the neighborhood to see if anyone needs my help with anything.

2. Your personal hero is:
- **A -** Frank Gehry
- **B -** Vincent Van Gogh
- **C -** Albert Einstein

3. Your prized possession is:
- **A -** My hammer
- **B -** My graphics programs
- **C -** My pretend badge

4. What's your dream vacation destination?
- **A -** Prague, to check out the architecture.
- **B -** Paris, to visit all the museums.
- **C -** New York City, to see the 9/11 Memorial.

5. What's your favorite type of TV show?
- **A -** Home improvement shows—I love to see what they build.
- **B -** Cartoons—they have the most awesome graphics.
- **C -** True crime, all the way.

Builder — Mostly As

You love to build stuff—you probably have all kinds of awesome tools. Your future career will be in architecture, where you can plan the building of structures or in actual construction, where you can be hands-on and do the building yourself.

Designer — Mostly Bs

You dig designing and drawing and love to appreciate others' creations, too. Your future career will be in graphic design or illustration. You'll design totally cool video games or cartoons or books and magazines.

Problem Solver — Mostly Cs

You love to get to the bottom of a problem and to rescue people in trouble. Your future career will be in law enforcement as a police officer or a detective, or in firefighting. You'll be able to help people in need and solve crimes every day of your life.

Super Fan

Are you a super seeker? Put your eyes to the test and see if you can find 10 differences between the picture on the top and the one on the bottom.

Answer on page 264

Sudoku
THINK TANK

Dive into the think tank and try to decode this sudoku. Fill in the empty squares so that each row, column, and square contains the numbers 1–9 only once.

9				6	1			
	8				5	4		1
	1		8	4	2			
4		3	1			8		
				9				
		1			4	3		9
			3	5	6		1	
3		6	2				4	
			4	7				5

Answer on page 264

Design Your BREAKFAST OF CHAMPIONS

Ever mix a whole bunch of different cereals together? What did your concoction taste like? What would you have named it? Here's your chance to design your own brand of cereal!

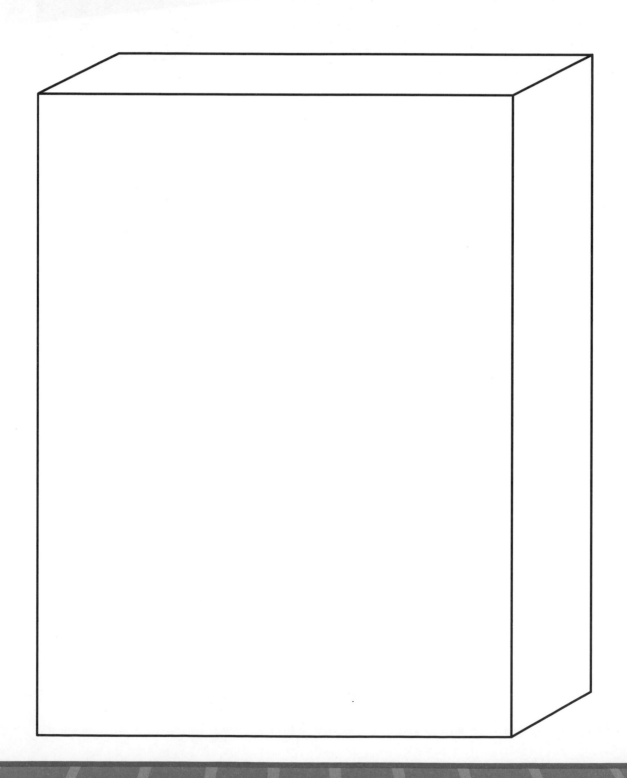

ZOMBIE ATTACK!

Search, find, and circle these 10 things.

BANANA PEEL **COWBOY BOOT** **SPOON**
BASKETBALL **EIGHT BALL** **TACO**
BUTTON **GOLF CLUB** **VIKING HELMET**
NICKEL

Baseball BASICS

Swing, batter, batter! It's time to learn the basics of baseball (and if you think you already know it all—it never hurts to brush up on your skills)!

THE BASICS

- A baseball game is played by two teams, each with nine players. The goal is to get enough hits and walks to round the bases and score more runs than your opponents.

THE EQUIPMENT

Mitt: A big leather glove that is used to catch the ball.
Baseball: A regulation baseball is three inches in diameter and has red stitching.
Bat: In professional baseball, players use wood bats (little league often uses metal bats).

THE FIELD

- The infield is the portion of the field closest to the bases.
- Anything beyond the bases is the outfield.
- Each base is ninety feet away from the next base.

DEFENSE – THE POSITIONS

Pitcher: Stands in the middle of the diamond and throws the ball to the batter.
Catcher: Squats behind the batter and catches any balls not hit (or foul balls in his territory). The catcher often tells the pitcher what kind of pitch to throw.
Infielders: The infielders are the first baseman, the second baseman, shortstop, and the third baseman.
Outfielders: The outfielders are the left fielder, the center fielder, and the right fielder.

THE GAME

- There are nine innings in professional baseball games.
- At the top of the inning, the home team fields and the visiting team is at bat. At the bottom of the inning, the opposite happens.
- Each team gets three outs per inning.

PLAYING OFFENSE

- The batting order cannot change during the game (but players can be substituted in).
- A batter gets three strikes per at bat.
- If the umpire calls four balls, the batter automatically advances to first base.
- A hit is technically when a player hits the balls and safely reaches a base without getting out or forcing another runner out.
- A homerun is a ball hit over the outfield walls, but within fair territory.

PLAYING DEFENSE

There are different ways the team on defense can get the other team out.

- Strikeouts (when a hitter misses three pitches)
- Force outs (when, after the ball is hit, the defensive player who caught or fielded the ball reaches a base before the runner)
- Fly outs (when a player hits the ball in the air and it's caught by a fielder before it hits the ground)
- Tag outs (when a runner is touched with the ball, or a glove with the ball in it)

Baseball Star

It's time to slide into home base! Can you find the two pictures that are exactly alike?

Answer on page 265

Write Your BLOG

What is the grossest thing you have ever done? What made it so memorable? Write a blog entry about it here!

SO GROSS!

Caption for your picture _____

_____

_____

_____

_____

_____

_____

_____

_____

_____

post by _____ time _____

Let's Draw a
Velociraptor

On a separate piece of paper, follow these simple steps using a pencil and an eraser.

1 Lightly sketch an egg-shaped oval for the body. Next, using oval guidelines, very carefully create the upper and lower jaws, then connect them to the body. Then add the tail.

2 Using simple shapes, draw the arms, legs, and claws. Note the upturned claw on each foot.

3 Add the eye and teeth. Then refine all the shapes into a smooth outline of Velociraptor.

4 Add the final touches. Experts believe that Velociraptor hunted in packs, so you might want to draw several of them attacking a giant plant-eating dinosaur.

Making WORDS

Show your book smarts. Can you make 25 or more words from the following phrase?

ACTION FIGURE

Answer on page 265

FaMiLY portrait

Are you a super seeker? Put your eyes to the test and see if you can find 10 differences between the picture on the top and the one on the bottom.

Answer on page 265

List Your Travelin' Places

Think about all of the awesome places you've been in your life so far. Answer these questions and you'll remember all kinds of cool stuff about your travels!

Where is the farthest you've ever traveled?

What is the most exotic place you've ever been?

What is your favorite place to visit?

Ever traveled by plane? If so, where did you fly?

Which destination was your least favorite?

What is your favorite way to travel?

Decode-a- RIDDLE

Write the letter that comes THREE LETTERS AFTER each letter shown below to decode and solve the riddle.

T E X Q   H F K A

L C   B X O P   A L

Q O X F K P   E X S B ?

B K D F K B B O P

VIDEO GAMES

Find these things that have to do with video games in the word search below. Look up, down, backward, forward, and diagonally.

| Arcade | Console | Gamer | Keyboard | Role playing |
| Computer | Controller | Joystick | Programmer | Television |

```
N Q Q Y C C L K K C F R U R
J O F P R O C W O H T E C O
E X I R I I N N N B T T T L
U B S S T G T S G F V U H E
A R T S I R Y A O C U P S P
P V Y P O V M G B L E M M L
G O L L F E E B N S E O G A
J R L Z R W S L V T W C V Y
K E Y B O A R D E F W A K I
R A M U K W X U X T I R U N
T N A F C S Y I J L I C M G
F J U Y R S R P U A U A F I
T G O Q B N B F J B S D X K
P R E M M A R G O R P E B Y
```

Design Your Own
VIDEO GAME

You know how, when you're playing a video game, you think of a million ways you would redo the game to make it even more awesome? Well, here's your chance to design your own video game!

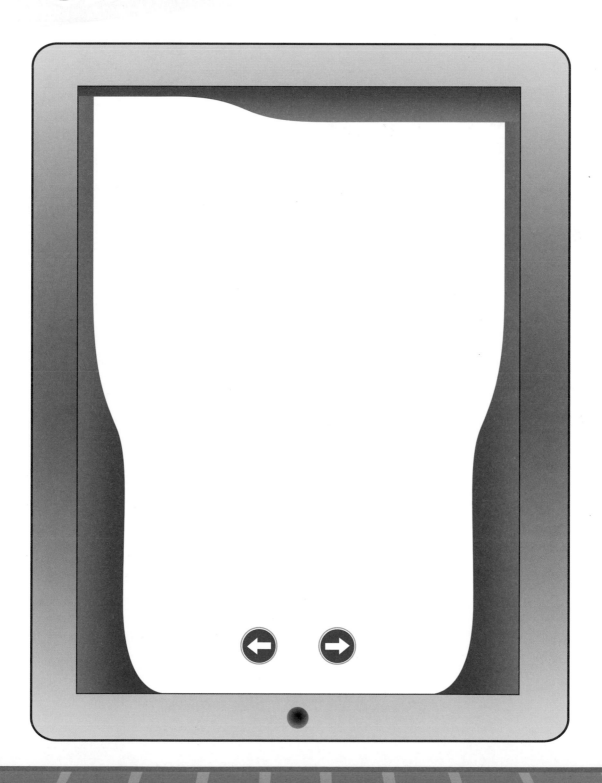

YUMMY BREAKFAST!

Use the clues about breakfast to complete this crossword puzzle.

ACROSS
1. Cooked bread
5. Round, flat, and yummy
6. You usually pour milk over this

DOWN
2. Made with eggs and other ingredients mixed in
3. Some people drink this instead of coffee
4. A meat you eat with eggs

Answer on page 266

Basketball Maze

Follow the correct path through the maze to get the basketball to the hoop. What's the correct path, you ask? It's the one that is made up of basketballs only.

START ↓

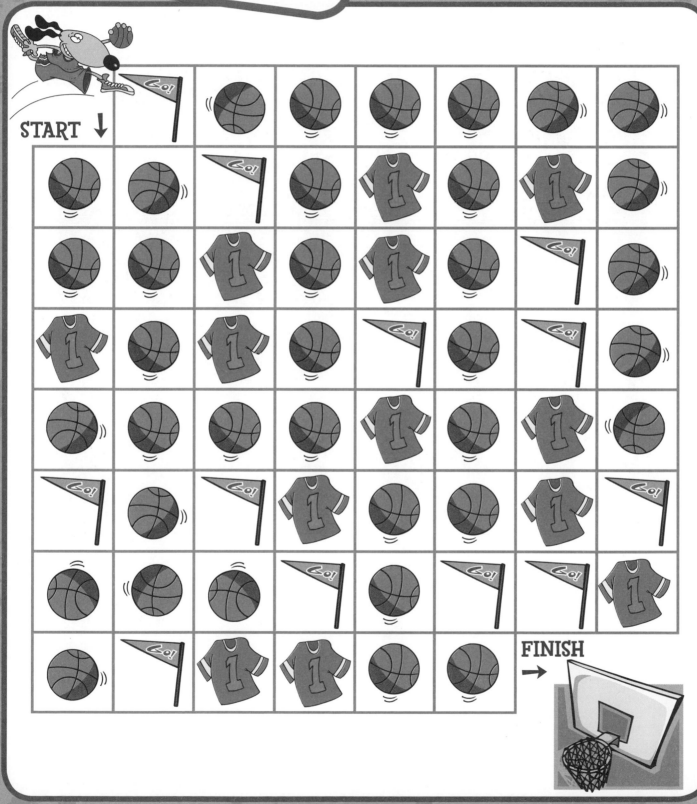

FINISH →

Skateboarding FACTS

Are you big into skateboarding, or is it something you've always wanted to try? Check out these fun skateboarding facts!

There are 18.5 million skateboarders in the world—74% of boarders are male.

Skateboarding started in California during the sixties as something for surfers to do when there wasn't a good swell in the ocean. The first skateboards looked a lot more like mini surfboards than the ones we know today, and skateboarding itself was called "sidewalk surfing."

Go Skateboarding Day was created in 2004 as a way for companies to make the public aware of the sport, and to inspire people to pick up a skateboard. Celebrate it every June 21!

In 1999, Tony Hawk became the first person to land a "900." The 900 is when you spin 900 degrees in midair—that's two and a half revolutions!

Super Skater

Let's skate! Can you find the two pictures that are exactly alike?

Let's Draw a
Goblin

On a separate piece of paper, follow these simple steps using a pencil and an eraser.

1 Begin with an egg shape for the head and add on basic shapes for the body and legs. Add an area for the loincloth and boots.

2 Add arms, ears, and a hat. Next, add guidelines for the face.

3 Draw the eyes, nose, and mouth. Erase the guidelines, and add bandages and a vest.

4 Draw a bone necklace. Add color and shading to complete your drawing.

CREATURE FEATURE

There is some serious mythical madness happening here! Find the names of these creatures in the word search below. Look up, down, backward, forward, and diagonally.

Bigfoot   **Dragon**   **Gnome**   **Mermaid**   **Ogre**
Centaur   **Gargoyle**   **Leprechaun**   **Mummy**   **Vampire**

```
N Y W C X S U R O A F B E S
W U Z Z N F U E G O R A L D
Y Z A Q W A R G A L S O Y E
F M W H T F B A A I Q J O U
Q B M N C V A M P I R E G E
N J E U I E D U D Q X K R S
M C Q Y M R R M G A B B A N
N E K H A V U P I V I E G K
J P R G C U D X E U G R F P
P Q O M E M O N G L F G C T
V N B V A X U E O T O O L C
O U E J Q I D Y X R O D Q W
W S R W T Q D S S P T F V Y
H F W Z D Z W J E U B E N M
```

Answer on page 267

Design Your Own
CREATE A CONVO

What is this kid saying to his mom—and what is Mom thinking when she sees this seriously messed-up gift? Fill out the thought bubbles.

Design Your Own
ALIEN NATION

It's years into the future, and aliens have invaded the planet. They pick you to help them run the new planet. Time to get to work!

Name of New Planet

_____

Leaders of New Planet

_____
_____
_____
_____
_____

Careers on New Planet

_____
_____

I AM A TEACHER

Laws of New Planet

_____
_____
_____

School Subjects on New Planet

_____
_____
_____

Currency on New Planet

_____

Holidays of New Planet

_____
_____
_____

Bouncy Castle

Jump, jump, jump! Can you find the two pictures that are exactly alike?

Answer on page 267

Sudoku
BRILLIANT BRAINIAC

Put your brilliant brain on display and try to decode this sudoku. Fill in the empty squares so that each row, column, and square contains the numbers 1–9 only once.

							5	6
3			5	2				
9		5			1	2		
		3		1	5	4		
	7		8		3		1	
	6	7	9		8			
	2	1				9		5
			4	8				1
6	8							

Answer on page 267

Decode-a-RIDDLE

Use the code key below to decode and solve this riddle.

1=A	7=G	13=M	19=S	23=W
2=B	8=H	14=N	20=T	24=X
3=C	9=I	15=O	21=U	25=Y
4=D	10=J	16=P	22=V	26=Z
5=E	11=K	17=Q		
6=F	12=L	18=R		

$\overline{23}$ $\overline{8}$ $\overline{1}$ $\overline{20}$ $\overline{19}$ $\overline{8}$ $\overline{15}$ $\overline{21}$ $\overline{12}$ $\overline{4}$

$\overline{5}$ $\overline{22}$ $\overline{5}$ $\overline{18}$ $\overline{25}$ $\overline{19}$ $\overline{12}$ $\overline{15}$ $\overline{16}$ $\overline{16}$ $\overline{25}$

$\overline{19}$ $\overline{16}$ $\overline{25}$ $\overline{8}$ $\overline{1}$ $\overline{22}$ $\overline{5}$ **?**

$\overline{1}$ $\overline{12}$ $\overline{9}$ $\overline{3}$ $\overline{5}$ $\overline{14}$ $\overline{19}$ $\overline{5}$

$\overline{20}$ $\overline{15}$ $\overline{19}$ $\overline{16}$ $\overline{9}$ $\overline{12}$ $\overline{12}$

Answer on page 267

Ups and Downs

Solve this rebus puzzle to discover the name of something that has its ups and downs.

-ICE+

-X+ -E+D

Snakes FACTS

Slithery and scaly and oh-so-cool, snakes are your thing, huh? Want to learn more about them? Check out these fun facts!

Snakes are related to lizards.

Snakes turn "blue" before they shed. This change in color is due to a layer of fluid between the old and new skins, right before the shed of the old skin.

Venom can be poisonous to the heart, nerves, and DNA.

Two kinds of snakes, the grass snake and the spitting cobra, can fake death by flipping on their backs when threatened.

A snake's heart can slide 1 to 1 ½ times its length from its normal position, to allow the passage of swallowed prey.

Slithering Snake

This snake's slithering his way home. What do you think his humble abode is like? Draw a home for this scaly snake!

LIVING on the MOON

Fill in the blanks to complete this silly story about what it might be like to live on the moon. Pick a NOUN, ADJECTIVE, or VERB from the word bank to place in a corresponding blank, or think of your own wacky words!

Believe it or not, living on the moon is kind of _____ and
[ADJECTIVE]

it is totally not at all _____, like most people would think.
[ADJECTIVE]

The _____ who reside on the moon spend most of their
[NOUN]

days _____ in the hopes of being the first people to make
[VERB]

_____. The trip from Earth to the moon is very _____.
[NOUN]   ADJECTIVE]

Come on up and _____ some time!
[VERB]

WORD BANK

ADJECTIVES

delicious
insane
creative
dangerous
intense
cool
silly
bent
loud

NOUNS

pork chops
guitars
basketballs
hooks
oatmeal
jars
brains
under wear
stones

VERBS

whisper
cram
chum
lick
squirm
hide
crouch
beep
sleep

Making WORDS

Can you make 25 or more words from the following word?

EXPEDITION

_____ _____

_____ _____

_____ _____

_____ _____

_____ _____

_____ _____

_____ _____

_____ _____

_____ _____

_____ _____

Do You Have Good Manners?

Are you polite or are you a little bit too rude? To find out, read each statement, then put a check under "True" or "False." When you're done, go to the end of the quiz to see your results!

	TRUE	FALSE
1. I try not to be too loud.	◯	◯
2. I cover my mouth when I cough.	◯	◯
3. I use a tissue or handkerchief when I sneeze.	◯	◯
4. I don't litter.	◯	◯
5. I always knock on a door before I enter a room.	◯	◯
6. I try my best never to insult people.	◯	◯
7. I never interrupt people when they are talking.	◯	◯

	TRUE	FALSE

8. I always use silverware, not my hands, to eat.

9. Words like "sorry" and "thank you" are a big part of my vocabulary.

10. I always respect my elders.

11. I never use foul language.

POLITE DUDE

If you chose mostly "True" answers, you are a polite guy, which is a good thing. People tend to gravitate toward people who are polite to them, because they feel comfortable around them. Keep it up.

RUDE AND CRUDE

If you chose mostly "False" answers, you're a little on the rude side. Try to tone it down and adopt some better manners. You'll be surprised what a difference it makes.

Calculate an ERA ////////////////

How To TIPS

Ever wonder how a baseball pitcher's ERA (Earned Run Average) is calculated? Here you go!

ERA Basics

1. Add up the total innings a pitcher pitched. For every out, you get one-third of an inning.

2. Now, add up the total number of earned runs given up. All the runs in an inning with no errors are earned runs. If there were errors in an inning, you have to go back and figure out how many runs would have scored had the fielding been perfect.

3. Next, multiply the earned runs by nine.

4. Divide that number by the number of total innings the pitcher pitched.

Write Your
BLOG

Do you have a secret that nobody knows about? What is it? And why do you keep it a secret? Write a blog entry about it here!

My Biggest Secret

Caption your picture _____

_____

_____

_____

_____

_____

_____

_____

_____

_____

post by_____ time _____

Let's Draw a
Treefolk

On a separate piece of paper, follow these simple steps using a pencil and an eraser.

1 Begin by drawing an apple core for the body.

2 Add an oval for the head. Next, draw the arms, hands, and legs.

3 Start to finalize the drawing by adding the face, hair, and root for toes. Add branches to the top of the head.

4 Draw the leaves, branch beard, and big shadow on the body. Finish the drawing with color and shading.

Werewolf Maze

Follow the path from **Start** to **Finish** to help the howling werewolf reach the moon.

FINISH

START →

Answer on page 268

WACKY WIZARDS

Search, find, and circle these 10 things.

BEARD
CAR
DALMATIAN

DUCK
FAIRY
FLYING PIG
HAMBURGERS (2)

ICE-CREAM SUNDAE
PIE
UNICORN

Answer on page 268

Design Your Own
AWESOME CITY

You've just been assigned to the City Planning Commission. Draw in the rest of this city and add stuff to the buildings that are already there. What else does this city need? Who are the people who live there?

Would You Rather...

Which would you rather do?
Look at each pair of options. Think about them and check the things you would like best. Ask your friends, too!

Would you rather...

☐ Drink mud   or   ☐ Eat chalk?

Would you rather be able to...

☐ Sing   or   ☐ Dance?

Would you rather have...

☐ One big brother   or   ☐ One big sister?

Would you rather skip...

☐ Christmas   or   ☐ Your birthday?

Let's Draw a
Monster Truck

On a separate piece of paper, follow these simple steps using a pencil and an eraser.

1 This monster truck starts with one basic body shape and four huge tire shapes. It is important to draw through those tire shapes so they are correct.

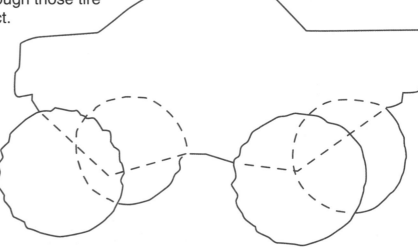

2 Establish the body by drawing the wheel wells, the truck bed, windows, and doors. Erase any unwanted lines to clean up the wheels and add rims.

3 Use lines to show tire treads and the giant shocks. Show chassis and rim details and add some cool graphics on the side.

4 Use a bright red and yellow color combination and make sure you show plenty of highlights on the big treads! This monster truck looks like it can roll over anything!

Make Cool Knots!

How To TIPS

Like the scouts say, it's always good to be prepared. You never know when you'll be in a situation that will require you to tie up some complicated knots. Check out these three knots and how to tie them!

THE SQUARE KNOT

This knot is used to bind things or hold them together.

THE BOWLINE

This knot is used to make a loop and it is often used for rescue missions.

After the bowline has been formed, you must tighten it correctly like this:

Tightened correctly

Tightened incorrectly

TWO HALF HITCHES

This knot can be used to tie almost anything.

TYPES OF KNOTS

Find these things that have to do with knots in the word search below. Look up, down, backward, forward, and diagonally.

Bowline **Figure eight** **Loop** **Reef knot** **Slip knot**

Coil **Half hitch** **Overhand** **Rope** **Square knot**

```
F X E Q S H M Z V Z T E I H
T I X G Q I H Q E I N G A C
O Y G V U P L U A I F L U O
N B K U A T P O L J F E W B
K N L B R O O W O H A Z R M
P G R Q E E O N I P R U V Y
I P R Q K B E T K O B L O R
L L O P N S C I T F C I N K
S X P U O H Y A G P E E S M
M D E Z T D D N A H R E V O
D Q K I J T B W N W T W R Y
C I K Z H W O H F U X J C A
V X T R L T K P I H Q P P A
T H N L F W Y Z C O I L M Q
```

Answer on page 269

Baseball Fever

Are you a super seeker? Put your eyes to the test and see if you can find 10 differences between the picture on the top and the one on the bottom.

Answer on page 269

Making
WORDS

Can you make 15 or more words of five or more letters from the following phrase?

HELICOPTER TRIP

Rock and Roll

It's time to rock and roll! Can you find the two pictures that are exactly alike?

Answer on page 269

•List Your Music Mania

List all of your favorite songs, artists, bands, and more right here. While you're at it, crank up your MP3 player!

My favorite bands:

When I'm in a good mood, I listen to:

My favorite songs of all time:

When I'm in a bad mood, I listen to:

The best CDs of all time:

The most awesome videos:

Sudoku
SMART AS A WHIP

You're smart as a whip, so try to decode this sudoku. Fill in the empty squares so that each row, column, and square contains the numbers 1–9 only once.

	5	4	6				7	
	9	6			7			
7			2			4		
5			4	7		6	3	
				1				
	1	2		9	8			4
		3			4			7
		7				9	6	
	7					2	4	

Mixed-up

STORIES

The story below is listed in the wrong order. Write the numbers of the correct order in the spaces below.

After learning about coral reefs, Roberto asks his parents if he can take scuba diving lessons.

1

Roberto makes a scrapbook of pictures he took with a special underwater camera.

2

Roberto and his parents fly to the Bahamas to learn to scuba dive.

3

_____

_____

_____

_____

_____

_____

Roberto sees his favorite kind of fish, a parrot fish.

4

Roberto writes a report for science class and becomes interested in coral reefs.

5

Roberto and his parents get on a boat headed away from their hotel in the Bahamas.

6

Answer on page 270

Explorer Maze

Follow the correct path through the maze to get the shark to the map. What's the correct path, you ask? It's the one that is made up of blue fish only!

START

FINISH

Answer on page 270

Decode-a- RIDDLE

Use the code key below to decode and solve this riddle.

1=A	8=H	15=O	22=V
2=B	9=I	16=P	23=W
3=C	10=J	17=Q	24=X
4=D	11=K	18=R	25=Y
5=E	12=L	19=S	26=Z
6=F	13=M	20=T	
7=G	14=N	21=U	

23 8 1 20   22 5 7 5 20 1 2 12 5

4 15   25 15 21   14 5 22 5 18

23 1 14 20   20 15   2 18 9 14 7

15 14   1   2 15 1 20 ?

1   12 5 1 11

Read a Compass

How To TIPS

Need some direction in your life? If you are ever lost or stranded, and happen to have a compass, you will need to know how to use it. Here's a step-by-step guide.

Compass Basics

1. Turn the compass until the North arrow on the face of the compass is lined up with the North side of the pointer. The compass is now aligned.

2. Now, look at the numbers. These are degrees, another way of measuring the compass direction.

3. Face any direction. Hold one of your hands out and place the compass flat in your palm. Point the arrow in the same direction you are facing.

4. Next, turn the dial on the compass so that the North-facing arrow is lined up with the pointer.

5. Read the degree mark that the index line goes across. That is your direction in degrees.

Use your compass know-how and create a cool map of your neighborhood.

SPORTS OF ALL SORTS

Play ball! Or, dive in! Whatever your sport of choice is, find the names of these sports in the word search. Look up, down, backward, forward, and diagonally.

Baseball   **Football**   **Hockey**   **Softball**   **Tennis**
Basketball   **Golf**   **Soccer**   **Swimming**   **Volleyball**

```
J B Q S S B F C H A S W L N
R V L U I C A L Q O O L Q S
K B L E B N M S F A A G I W
I N A R S X N T E B H H E I
O I B G J C B E T U B M M
J F Y H P A U E T U A K E M
Y P E A L V K T R T F L B I
E I L L C S R E C C O S L N
K E L T A F O O T B A L L G
C B O B F Y K G Y N I A K Z
O M V L D O D I T I G X M D
H F O K F R T I W H D U Y D
Y G W O W C N M Q H O Y E M
V T C U W Z R N O M Q N F W
```

Answer on page 271

Wrestling FACTS

Most people know that wrestling is a professional sport, but did you know that the sport itself goes back a long, long time? Enhance your wrestling knowledge with these fun facts!

The word "wrestling" originated as a term for hand-to-hand combat in Old English. It dates back before 1100 A.D., and is one of the oldest words in the modern English language that still retains its original meaning!

Wrestling was a popular sport in ancient Greece, and is most associated with this era because it was the top sport of the early Olympic games. However, wrestling goes back 15,000 years— we know this because cave drawings in France show people wrestling!

Sumo is an ancient form of Japanese wrestling in which two opponents try to force each other outside of a ring. Sumo still exists today, but in the 1600s, most sumo wrestlers were unemployed samurai who needed a source of income. Even warriors need to work!

BEST WRESTLING

Fill in the blanks to complete this silly story about inventing your own signature wrestling move. Pick a NOUN, ADJECTIVE, or VERB from the word bank to place in a corresponding blank, or think of your own wacky words!

Forget about all the wrestling moves you've seen before—I've

come up with the most _____ move ever! In order to perform
[ADJECTIVE]

this super- _____ move, you have to _____ your opponent
[ADJECTIVE]   [VERB]

and then _____ and _____ the _____. If you try it and
[VERB]   [VERB]   [NOUN]

wind up in a _____, head to the doctor immediately!
[NOUN]

GRRRRR!!

WORD BANK

ADJECTIVES
tight
swell
beautiful
intricate
weird
wild
cold
blue
little

NOUNS
heap
pile
pretzel
bucket
fence
squirrel
tree
drawer
noggin

VERBS
slam
kick
lift
look
nap
run
sweat
burn
bend

NO SCHOOL TODAY!

Use the clues below to complete this crossword puzzle about days when you don't have school.

ACROSS
1. Season between Spring and Fall
2. Special type of "day" like Christmas or Easter
3. When you have a cold or toothache, you're _____.
4. When parents meet with teachers
5. Teachers go to these group events to discuss stuff.

DOWN
1. You do a lot of digging in these types of storms.

Let's Draw a

Stegosaurus

On a separate piece of paper, follow these simple steps using a pencil and an eraser.

1 Start by drawing your Stegosaurus by lightly sketching these basic shapes: first, a large oval, then two smaller ovals and a triangle.

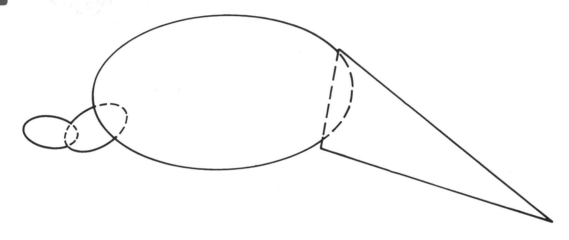

2 Draw some triangles on the tail and diamond-shaped plates on the back. Add ovals for the legs and feet.

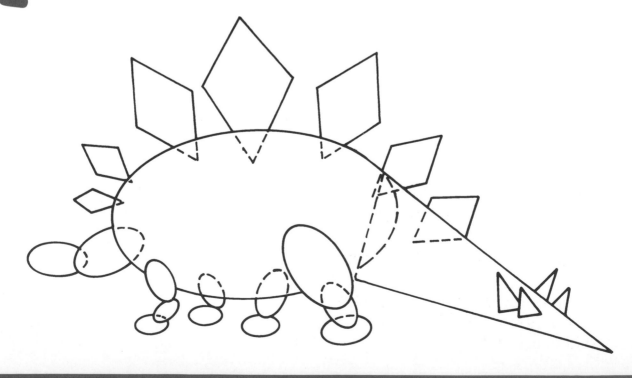

3 Take all your guidelines and blend them into this dinosaur's basic shape. Erase any unnecessary lines so that you have a clean line drawing of your Stegosaurus.

4 Put the finishing touches on your drawing. Add texture to the back plates and some spots to Stegosaurus's back.

Hockey TERMS

Grab your hockey stick and get ready to hit the ice! But, before you do, brush up on all of these important hockey terms. You'll go pro in no time at all!

Attacking Zone: The area of the ice that goes from the blue line to the end boards and belongs to the opposing team.

Backhand: Pass shot that is hit with the back of the stick's blade.

Blocker: A rectangular pad that the goalie wears on the hand he uses to hold his stick.

Boarding: Slamming, or checking, a player roughly into the boards. This is a penalty.

Boards: The walls surrounding the playing area of the ice.

Breakaway: When a player is in possession of the puck and there are no opposing players, except the goalie, between him and the goal.

Center: A player whose main area of play is the center of the ice.

Cherry Picking: This is when a player stays near the other team's goal waiting for someone to pass him the puck in order to make a breakaway shot.

Clipping: Hitting an opponent below the knees.

Face-off: This is how the game starts at the beginning of each period. Both teams line up across from each other and one player from each teams tries to get possession of the puck after it is dropped, by an official, between the teams.

Goal: When the puck goes totally into the goal frame, past the goal line, it is considered a goal.

Hat Trick: This is when a player scores three goals in a single game.

Hip Check: When a player uses his hip to bump an opponent.

Overtime: When, at the end of a regulation game, the score is tied, extra time is added. This is called overtime. The game is won by the first team to score a goal in overtime.

Penalty Box: This is the area a player sits in when a penalty is charged to him.

Power Play: When players are charged with penalties, and are in the penalty box, the other team has more players on the ice during that time. This is a power play.

Rebound: This is when the puck bounces off of the goalie, a player or the net after a shot.

Referee: This is the person in charge of officiating the game and making sure everyone is playing by the rules.

Saucer Pass: A saucer pass is when one player passes the puck, in the air and not on the ice, to another player.

Slap Shot: A very hard shot that is made when a player slaps his stick against the ice to launch the puck.

Wrist Shot: This is a shot taken with the open-faced part of the stick.

Zone: The three different areas of the ice, as divided by blue lines. The three zones are the attacking zone, neutral zone, and the defensive zone.

HOCKEY STUFF

Use the clues about hockey to solve the crossword puzzle.

ACROSS
4. This happens when one team has more players on the ice than the other.
6. This is used to decide the winning team; players take turns trying to score.
7. To do this is to bump another player out of the way.

DOWN
1. This player tries to keep the other team from scoring.
2. A player gets this if he violates a rule.
3. A hard-hitting shot at the goal from a distance away
5. This is what all the players scramble to get.

Answer on page 271

Sudoku
SUPER STRENGTH

Try to decode this super tough sudoku. Fill in the empty squares so that each row, column, and square contains the numbers 1–9 only once.

		5					6	1
		3		6		2		5
			5				9	3
	3	1		9	8			2
7			4		5			6
			2	7		3	5	
	4				3			
3		7		8		1	2	4
2	9					6		

What's Your Color?

Did you know that color preference says a lot about you? What color best suits you and your personality? Take this quiz to determine your color.

Passionate   Calm   Mysterious

1. The word that best describes me is:
- **A -** Fun.
- **B -** Loyal.
- **C -** Secretive.

2. My favorite season is:
- **A -** Summer.
- **B -** Fall.
- **C -** Winter.

3. When on a team:
- **A -** I am just one of the guys.
- **B -** My plays make others look great.
- **C -** I like to be in charge.

4. Let's talk about fights:
- **A -** I start them.
- **B -** I mediate them.
- **C -** I end them.

5. Do you think you will ever get a tattoo?:
- **A -** Maybe.
- **B -** Never.
- **C -** Can't wait.

6. What kind of pet do you have?:
- **A -** Pit bull.
- **B -** Beagle.
- **C -** Saint Bernard.

Passionate—Mostly As

Your color is definitely red. You are passionate about stuff and go after whatever it is that you want at the moment.

Calm—Mostly Bs

Your signature color is blue, for sure. You are calm and peaceful and one of the most loyal guys out there!

Mysterious—Mostly Cs

Your signature color is purple, no doubt about it. You have an air of mystery about you and like to live on the edge and crave power.

BIRTHDAY PARTY

Search, find, and circle these 10 things.

BLUE CAKE

BUTTERFLY

DIAMOND

DUCK

EYEGLASSES

FISH

FORKS (3)

ICE-CREAM CONE

SNAKE

TEDDY BEAR

Answer on page 272

OUT OF THIS WORLD

There's a whole new world out there in outer space! Find the names of these planets and their galaxy in the word search below. Look up, down, backward, forward, and diagonally.

Earth	Mars	Milky Way	Saturn	Venus
Jupiter	Mercury	Neptune	Uranus	

M N E B Y L M M S W O T G S
N I R W C O W E U F B V U S
A X L U S C X R N J H N Z J
X X I K T Y Y C A G E C U J
R A C U Y A N U R V Q P M H
E A R T H W S R U I I T R P
N Q H Y A Y A F T W L R K
E N U T P E N Y E X T X S P
J J N O M I V R N E R V R B
A C D W Q D P O B X C O A B
Q K A C Y J U L B H R U M Q
R Y U L Z F V X U B U P G H
P W L U C X D U G T I Q I U
K L Z V M V Z M S T O N A Y

SNOW Day

Are you a super seeker? Put your eyes to the test and see if you can find 10 differences between the picture on the top and the one on the bottom.

Answer on page 272

Out on the Lake

Solve this rebus puzzle to discover a leisurely pastime on a lake.

_ _ _ _ _ _ _ _

Lucky Lottery

Imagine winning a billion dollars in the lottery. What would you do with all that dough? Make your wish list here, so you'll be prepared when you strike it rich!

The first thing I would buy is:

Charities I'd donate to:

I would buy my parents:

I would hire a:

Friends I'd give some cash to:

Dart FACTS

People all around the world play darts—and it's been around for a super long time. Want to learn more this cool sport? Check out these awesome dart facts.

The first version of a dart was likely just an arrow, used with either a bow or crossbow, cut down to a smaller size. The first darts made specifically for the game of darts were produced in France and were decorated with turkey feathers.

The Pilgrims played darts on the Mayflower! They brought the game with them to America, along with another game still played today— horseshoes.

Before World War I, dartboards were made from blocks of wood, rather than the cork or fiber used today. This meant that you had to soak the dartboard each night to "heal" the holes made by the darts—otherwise you wouldn't be able to play!

Let's Draw a
Gargoyle

On a separate piece of paper, follow these simple steps using a pencil and an eraser.

1 Draw a large oval for the head, arms, and legs. Add the legs, as shown.

2 Next, lightly sketch the head and arms, as shown.

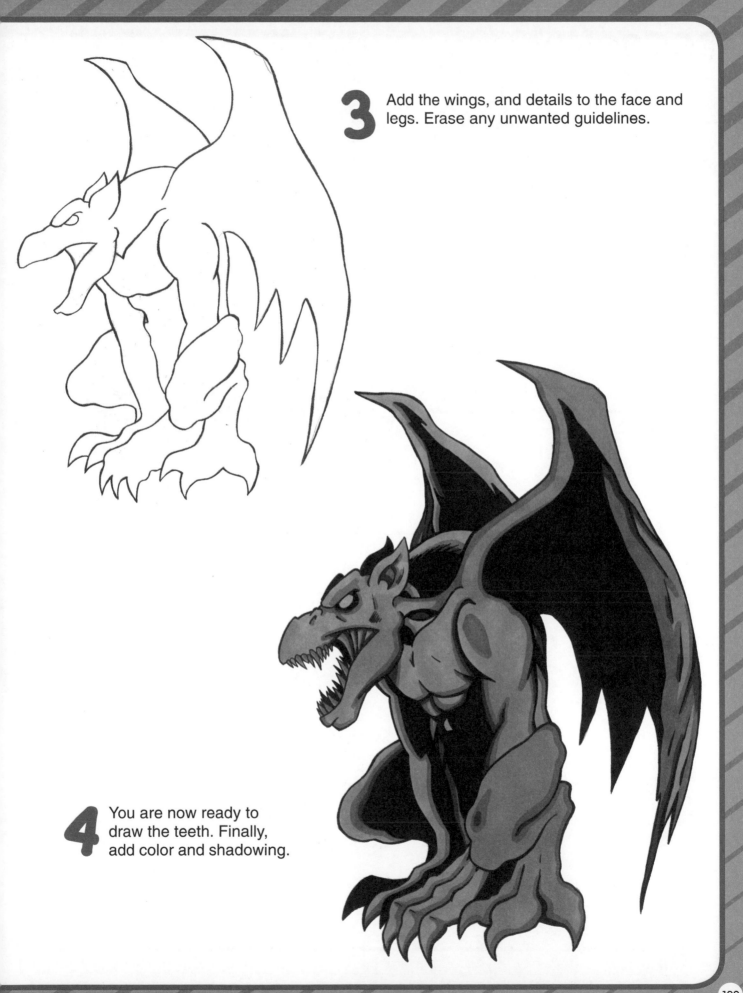

3 Add the wings, and details to the face and legs. Erase any unwanted guidelines.

4 You are now ready to draw the teeth. Finally, add color and shadowing.

Decode-a-RIDDLE

Use the code key below to decode and solve this riddle.

1=A	7=G	13=M	19=S	22=V
2=B	8=H	14=N	20=T	23=W
3=C	9=I	15=O	21=U	24=X
4=D	10=J	16=P		25=Y
5=E	11=K	17=Q		26=Z
6=F	12=L	18=R		

GARAGE SALE

__ __ __ __   __ __   __ __ __
23 8 1 20   4 15   25 15 21

__ __   __ __ __ __   __ __
 4 15   23 9 20 8   1 14

__ __ __   __ __ __ __ ?
15 12 4   2 9 11 5

__ __ __
25 15 21

__ __ - __ __ __ __ __   __ __
18 5   3 25 3 12 5   9 20

Answer on page 273

Ice-Cream Truck

Are you a super seeker? Put your eyes to the test and see if you can find 10 differences between the picture on the top and the one on the bottom.

Answer on page 273

Puppy Maze

Follow the correct path through the maze to get the dog to the bone. What's the correct path, you ask? It's the one that is made up of paw prints only!

START

FINISH

Answer on page 273

Making WORDS

Use your travel smarts. Can you make 25 or more words from the following word?

GLOBE-TROTTER

GO, GO, GO

Rev up your engine and find the names of these vehicles in the word search below. Look up, down, backward, forward, and diagonally.

Airplane   **Car**   **Monster truck**   **Rickshaw**   **Wagon**

Big rig   **Helicopter**   **Motorcycle**   **Taxi**   **Yacht**

```
E W G G V G P C V H B M J W
U N I D I U B C E H B O G A
S D A R K N F L C X M N J H
T O G L U T I A T H H S G S
P I H U P C M A Z E F T P K
B H C H O R Y A C H T E E C
D A U P W V I P Z D N R O I
R A T K R A O A U Y T T N R
R E K K V N G Z P S N R X E
R E L C Y C R O T O M U C H
G M E B Y K U N N Z J C S T
I A C I L C A N H P L K T A
N Q P N N N F C Y M E C O X
S J A G Q E J M K N I R U I
```

Answer on page 274

CAR PARTS

Use the clues about car parts to complete this crossword puzzle.

ACROSS
2. Storage space in back
4. Helps the driver see around the car
7. Plays music
9. The "shoes" of the car
10. Needed for driving at night

DOWN
1. The "heart" of the car
3. Makes the car stop
5. Keeps everyone in the car safe
6. Lets other drivers know where you are
8. Pops out if there's an accident

Answer on page 274

Dinosaur Maze

It's a prehistoric flashback! Follow the path from **Start** to **Finish** to guide the baby dinosaur to its mother.

START

FINISH

Answer on page 274

Write Your

BLOG

What do you want to be when you grow up? How do you plan on making it happen? Write a blog entry about it here!

When I Grow Up!

Caption your picture _____

_____

_____

_____

_____

_____

_____

_____

_____

_____

post by_____ time _____

GOLF

Grab your club and find these golf terms in the word search below. Look up, down, backward, forward, and diagonally.

Ball	Club	Green	Par	Swing
Birdie	Course	Iron	Score	Wood

```
F R P X A E K O C P K G G
D F J C E L X W O W A P J
L S T E S W N R U N C R B
A K Z L L A B K R P A X G
I P L A N V J V S I M C C
F A Y E B Q W W E N T K O
V C E U N H W O F O I S S
D R L E B O Z L U J J O C
G C L W O I I R O N B X O
M F V D V V R R B X G A R
C O G C E M A D S E H N E
B C R P W X C B I P J G C
T J L S W I N G G E B H Y
```

Answer on page 274

Cool Tree House

Are you a super seeker? Put your eyes to the test and see if you can find 10 differences between the picture on the top and the one on the bottom.

Answer on page 275

Are You Cut Out for Camping?

	TRUE	FALSE
1. If I could, I would be outdoors all day long.	◯	◯
2. I can build a fire.	◯	◯
3. Insects don't bother me.	◯	◯
4. I don't need a comfy bed to sleep well.	◯	◯
5. I can go days without showering.	◯	◯
6. I don't need gourmet meals.	◯	◯
7. Extreme temperatures don't affect me.	◯	◯

	TRUE	FALSE
8. I have a good sense of direction.	◯	◯
9. I don't need to watch TV.	◯	◯
10. I know the difference between poison ivy and poison oak.	◯	◯
11. I know how to find the North Star.	◯	◯

EXPERT CAMPER

If you chose mostly "True" answers, you are a camper at heart. Sleeping in a tent, even if it's raining, wouldn't faze you in the least. You have what it takes to be an expert camper!

CAMPING ROOKIE

If you chose mostly "False" answers, you might want to rethink that camping trip. You like creature comforts, and camping means roughing it. But, give it a try, anyway—you never know!.

Create Your OWN LIST

Sure, girls aren't all that bad, but it's really cool to be a boy. What makes being a boy so cool? List all the reasons you can think of in the blanks.

It's Great Being a Boy Because:

Mixed-up STORIES

The story below is listed in the wrong order. Write the numbers of the correct order in the spaces below.

1. Mark cooks some food in a special pot that hangs over his campfire.

2. Mark sets up his tent on the flattest spot.

3. Mark pours water over his campfire and stirs the ashes to make sure it is out.

4. Mark sweeps away any sticks and rocks so that his tent can lie flat.

5. Mark makes sure all his food is sealed up so animals don't bother him as he sleeps.

6. Mark gathers water to keep near his campfire, and small sticks to get the fire started.

___ ___ ___ ___ ___ ___

Identify Animal Tracks

How To TIPS

Do you know the difference between a dog track and a coyote track? It's good info to have—if you want to stay safe!

Animal Tracks Guide

Track Pattern

Hind	Front	Hind	Front	Hind	Front	Hind	Front
Bobcat		Coyote		Dog		Gray Fox	

Hind	Front	Hind	Front				
House Cat		Red Fox		White-Tailed Deer		Moose	

Track Pattern

Hind	Front	Hind	Front	Hind	Front
Otter		Fisher		Weasel	

Track Pattern

Hind	Front	Hind	Front	Hind	Front	Hind	Front
Raccoon		Striped Skunk		Porcupine		Beaver	

Hind	Front	Hind	Front	Hind	Front	Hind	Front
Black Bear		Opossum		Woodchuck		Muskrat	

Track Pattern

Hind	Front	Hind	Front	Hind	Front	Hind	Front
Snowshoe Hare		Cottontail Rabbit		Gray Squirrel		White-Footed Mouse	

MISCELLANOUS

Turkey	Crow	Ruffed Grouse

"B" THERE OR "B" SQUARE

Who knew there were so many countries that begin with the letter "B?" Find the names of these countries in the word search below. Look up, down, backward, forward, and diagonally.

Bahamas   **Bangladesh**   **Belgium**   **Bolivia**   **Brazil**

Bali   **Barbados**   **Bermuda**   **Bosnia**   **Bulgaria**

```
Q H C L Z T B U A F L I B G
M Q S X P A R I T R Y W O V
W N X E H O R F Y P A U L R
B Y G A D A U O L Z W S I C
J N M J G A G B I I R O V J
U A A L Z T L H A Z Z D I Y
S B U L B E L G I U M A A T
Q B E X U V X S N Y A B R T
C C V R Q Q F V Z A W R A B
Z Z Z S M F S L I M B A A P
B B T R H U A I N S O B I E
M U Q O E H D O N I U J L Q
R H P W I J L A H Q C N A M
Z K Y T Y N N C S C K V B R
```

SOUVENIRS

Use the clues about different kinds of souvenirs to complete this crossword puzzle.

Wish you were here!

ACROSS
1. Dangles from a ring
3. Send this to a friend
5. Sticks to the fridge
6. Pull this over your head to show others where you've visited

DOWN
2. Goes on top of your head
3. Hang this on your wall
4. Be careful not to poke your finger with this!
5. Sip something from this

RAD ROBOT

Fill in the blanks to complete this silly story about what it might be like have a robot. Pick a NOUN, ADJECTIVE, or VERB from the word bank to place in a corresponding blank, or think of your own wacky words!

I built the most _____ robot in my basement last week.
[ADJECTIVE]

He is made of my _____ and _____
[NOUN]   [NOUN]

and he is _____. My favorite thing he does is when
[ADJECTIVE]

he _____s. But it's also pretty funny to see him
[VERB]

_____ my _____. Even my parents like him!
[VERB]   [NOUN]

I can't wait to _____ him to all my _____s.
[VERB]   [NOUN]

WORD BANK

ADJECTIVES
warm
awesome
pink
tall
round
smart
stinky
strong
squiggly

NOUNS
friend
nose
book
poster
laptop
bedroom
elephant
skateboard
lollipop

VERBS
clean
cook
sniffle
knock
twirl
shine
sip
squeal
burn

Rebus RUCKUS

Solve this rebus puzzle to discover the name of something that you hear around a stable.

" _ _ _ _ _ _ _ _ _ _ "

Sudoku
PERFECT SKILLS

Show off your skills and try to decode this sudoku. Fill in the empty squares so that each row, column, and square contains the numbers 1–9 only once.

		9		1		2		7
8			2	6		1	9	
1	4		9					8
	4					6		
	9		3		1		8	
	1			8				2
7		5			4	8	1	9
	6			5	2			3
4		8		9		5		

Would You Rather...

Which would you rather do?
Look at each pair of options. Think
about them and check the things you
would like best. Ask your friends, too!

Would you rather give up...

☐ **Your bike**   or   ☐ **Your computer?**

Would you rather dye your hair...

☐ **Blue**   or   ☐ **Pink?**

Would you rather have...

☐ **Candy**   or   ☐ **Ice cream?**

Would you rather be...

☐ **A dog**   or   ☐ **A cat?**

Yo-Yo Tricks
How To
TIPS

A yo-yo trick, when done right, will impress your pals (and maybe that girl you have a crush on)! Here are some cool yo-yo tricks for you to try.

GRAVITY PULL

- Put the string around your middle finger.
- Your palm should be facing up.
- Throw the yo-yo down and lift your arm up, like you are making a muscle.
- When the yo-yo hits the bottom of the string, turn your palm down.
- Tug the yo-yo back up into your hand.

FORWARD PASS

- Put your hand behind your back, palm up.
- Release the yo-yo and bring your hand forward quickly.
- The yo-yo will go out in front of you.
- Pull it back to your hand and catch it.

THE SLEEPER

- Hold your yo-yo hand out with your palm and string facing up.
- Whip the yo-yo sharply toward the ground, like you're throwing a fastball.
- Have the yo-yo stay down—spinning—at the end of the string. While the yo-yo is spinning, turn your yo-yo hand over, palm facing down.
- You're doing it right if the yo-yo spins at the end of the string for a few seconds. Finally, give the string a jerk and the yo-yo should return to your hand.

THE WIND-UP

- Start with the yo-yo on the ground, still, not spinning.
- Pull it up as fast as you can.

LOOP THE LOOP

- Begin by throwing a forward pass.
- But, as the yo-yo comes back, do not catch it.
- Instead, turn your wrist and flick it back out.

ALL ABOUT YO-YOS!

Use the clues about yo-yos to complete this crossword puzzle.

$e = mc^2$

ACROSS

3. A move where your yo-yo "walks" on the ground; 3 words

4. A move where you start with the yo-yo on the ground; 2 words

5. A move where you let the yo-yo hang before flicking it back up; 2 words

6. A move where you flick the yo-yo down and let it hang and spin

DOWN

1. A move where you don't catch the yo-yo and let it fling around; 3 words

2. A move where you release the yo-yo behind you, then pull it forward; 2 words

Answer on page 276

Ahoy, Matey!

Yo ho ho! Can you find the two pictures that are exactly alike?

Answer on page 276

Darts Maze

Follow the path from **Start** to **Finish** to guide the dart thrower to the bullseye.

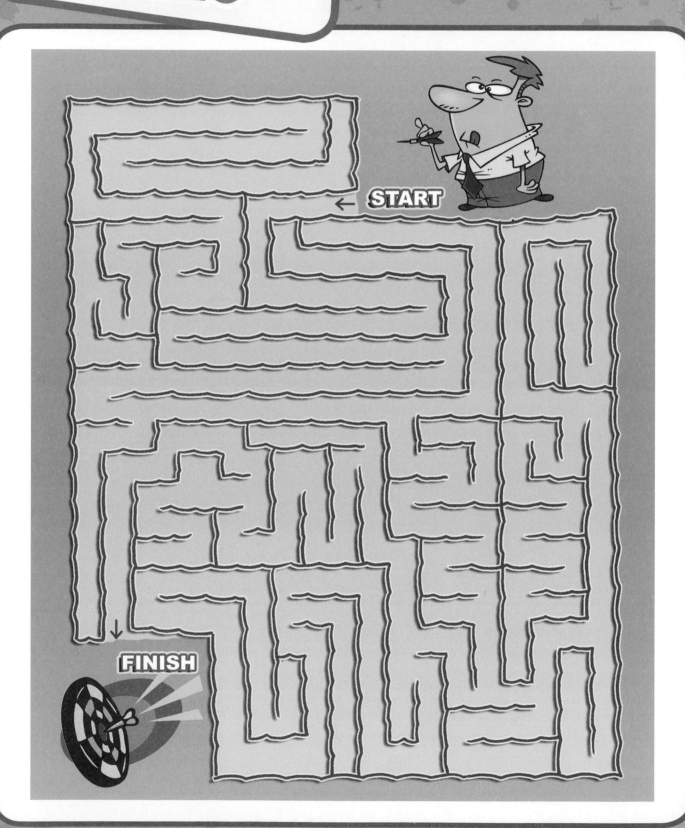

← START

↓

FINISH

Answer on page 277

Mixed-up STORIES

The story below is listed in the wrong order. Write the numbers of the correct order in the spaces below.

1. A family listens to a tour guide talk about ancient ruins.

2. A family gets on a bus and takes their seats.

3. A family asks a tour guide to take their picture so they can always remember their trip.

4. A family wakes up in their hotel.

5. A tour guide asks if anyone has any questions.

6. A family arrives at the site of some famous ruins.

— — — — — —

Create Your ADVENTURE LIST

The world is a big, cool, interesting place. You could spend your whole life traveling and still not see the whole world. What are your dream destinations? List them!

Places I Want To Travel To:

_____   _____

_____   _____

_____   _____

_____   _____

_____   _____

_____   _____

_____   _____

_____   _____

TRUCKIN' AROUND

Search, find, and circle these 10 things.

ALLIGATOR
BASEBALL CAPS (3)
BASKETBALL

FISHBOWL
MONKEY
SET OF GOLF CLUBS
SKATEBOARD

SLIDE
SOCCER BALL
TRUMPET

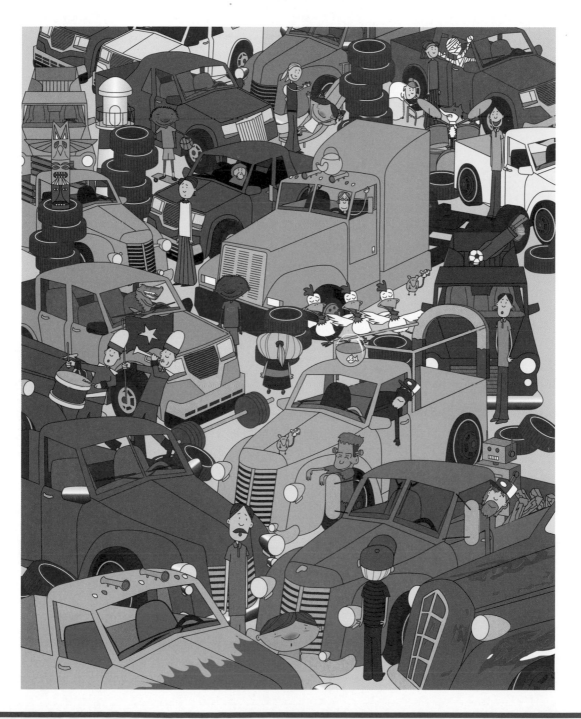

Answer on page 277

Let's Draw a
Porsche Boxster

On a separate piece of paper, follow these simple steps using a pencil and an eraser.

1 Begin by drawing the body car, canopy, and tires. Use guidelines to keep shapes accurate.

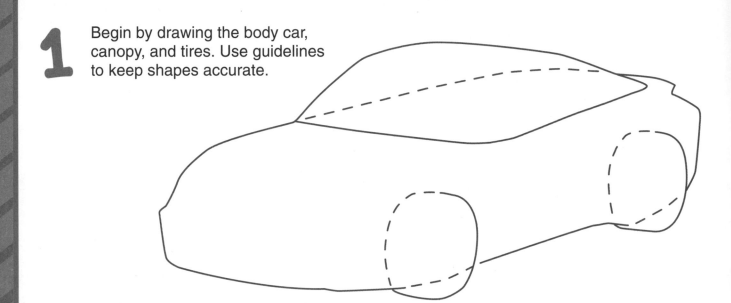

2 Erase the guideline. Next, draw the wheel wells, door, windows, and front bumper area. Add the front lights.

3 Draw interior details, glass door handle, and mirrors. Add hood detail and rims.

4 A yellow base with light and dark shadowing and black around the lights looks great. Add the black interior color with some gray accents, and head out to the highway.

ALL-STAR HOCKEY

Grab your hockey stick and find these hockey terms in the word search below. Look up, down, backward, forward, and diagonally.

Assist   **Goalie**   **Overtime**   **Pass**   **Puck**
Breakaway   **Interference**   **Pad**   **Penalty**   **Rebound**

```
B L O B I B N C M W M D S O
V P J E I X U C M K C U P P
E C N E R E F R E T N I L L
J P A S S Z W B U F E K G J
F H K G Z T P M Q Z P T R V
E Q A K Y A W A K A E R B E
K M A W D W B T D F B Q F Q
L Z I A R E B O U N D A L T
V B G T S N Y T L A N E P A
V R T O R S D C K A E W W Y
X R H Q A E I V S I C L J D
H I Z P F L V S X Q D D V Q
L A R M F N I O T D D J S Z
W B M F E L S E U P N F M H
```

Answer on page 277

Fright Night

Are you a super seeker? Put your eyes to the test and see if you can find 10 differences between the picture on the top and the one on the bottom.

Answer on page 278

Build a Blanket Fort!

How To TIPS

This is a super-fun thing to do when you have your friends over. You'll have hours of fun in a blanket fort! Be sure to ask an adult for help and supervision.

Blanket Fort Basics

1. It's always a good idea to ask your parents for permission first.

2. Pick an out-of-the-way area so that it's not in anyone's way. So, don't build it on the stairs, in a busy hallway, or in your bathtub!

3. Don't use items that somebody in the house might need.

4. Grab a few chairs and some sheets and/or blankets. If there are no chairs available, you could use the back of a couch or other furniture like that. It has to be a place that will hold your blanket well.

5. If you use chairs, situate them in a wide circle. If they are too close together, your fort could come crashing down.

6. Use safety pins to connect the sheets and blankets together. Be sure to ask an adult for help.

7. Drape the sheets and blankets over the top of the couches. Use clips or clothespins to keep the blankets on.

8. Leave an opening on the side of your fort for a door.

9. Leave an opening at the front and back of your fort for an entrance and an exit.

10. Place heavy objects along the edges of the sheets and blankets to hold them in place.

11. Pillows are good to use for walls or seats. Add a blanket and a few pillows inside to sit on.

What Animal Are You Most Like?

There are all sorts of personalities, and some people's traits can be compared to those of animals. Take this quiz to find out what kind of animal you're like.

Tiger   Golden Retriever   Turtle

1. You argue with your dad. You:
A - Go nuts and throw stuff.
B - Sulk for a while. Then talk it out.
C - Hide for a while, then never bring it up again.

2. Your sport of choice is:
A - Wrestling.
B - Baseball.
C - Golf.

3. Your favorite music is:
A - Heavy Metal.
B - Top 40.
C - Jazz.

4. Your friends:
A - Are sort of scared of you.
B - Love hanging out with you.
C - You don't have many friends.

5. Your favorite color is:
A - Black.
B - Blue.
C - White.

6. In school, your favorite subject is:
A - Math.
B - Gym.
C - Science.

Tiger—Mostly As

You are most like a tiger. You can be ferocious and tend to pounce on unsuspecting victims. Keep your fierceness, but tone it down a bit.

Golden Retriever—Mostly Bs

You are most like a golden retriever. You are loyal and loved and enjoy hanging out with your friends and doing guy stuff.

Turtle—Mostly Cs

You are most like a turtle. You are solitary and keep to yourself. It's okay to come out of your shell once in while!

TYPES OF SPIDERS

Use the clues about spiders to complete this crossword puzzle.

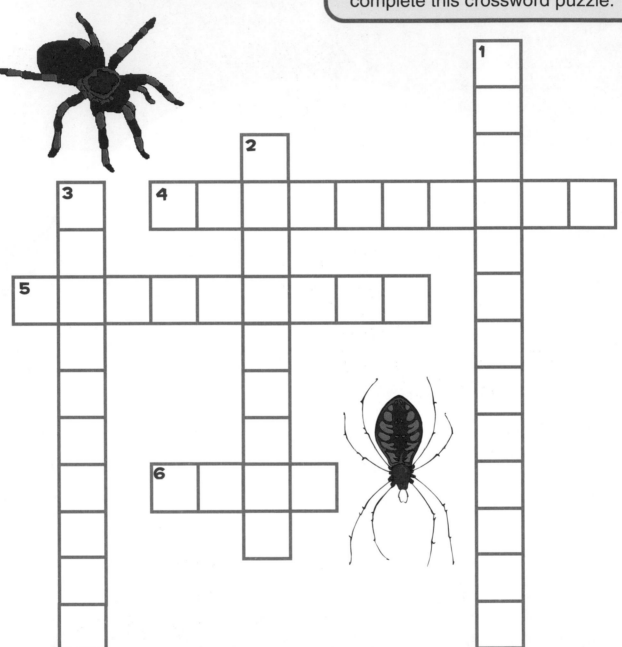

ACROSS

4. Very poisonous; 2 words
5. Named for its sphere-shaped web; 2 words
6. _____ spider; named after a fierce canine

DOWN

1. Named for the length of its limbs; 3 words
2. This type is sometimes a pet
3. Named for what it eats; 2 words (Hint: "It's a _____, it's a plane!")

Spider FACTS

Sure, they are spooky, creepy, and sometimes scary. But, spiders are do-gooders, too! Check out all of these fascinating spider facts!

Spiders are members of the arachnid family.

Most spiders use their fangs to inject the insect they are going to eat with venom. The venom will either instantly kill the prey or paralyze it. The spider then sprays digestive juices onto the solid tissue of the prey, which dissolves the tissue so that the spider can eat it.

Each year, on average, one person in the United States and three people in Europe die from spider bites.

Spiders can actually be pretty useful to humans. Spiders eat mosquitoes, which carry disease.

VIDEO DREAM

Fill in the blanks to complete this silly story about what it might be like to have a dream about living in your favorite video game. Pick a NOUN, ADJECTIVE, or VERB from the word bank to place in a corresponding blank, or think of your own wacky words!

You'll never believe this, but I had a dream that I was a part of my

favorite video game! It was the most _____ dream ever. I wore a
[ADJECTIVE]

_____ _____ and had a _____ as a weapon.
[ADJECTIVE]   [NOUN]   [NOUN]

Everyone around me was _____ and I had to _____ just
[ADJECTIVE]   [VERB]

to stay alive. I was never so _____ to wake up in my entire life!
[ADJECTIVE]

I can't wait to _____ again and go on another _____!
[VERB]   [NOUN]

WORD BANK

ADJECTIVES

sweet
sour
large
striped
red
sick
strange
spicy
quiet

NOUNS

violin
golf ball
puck
wig
fork
engine
umbrella
salt
strawberry

VERBS

shout
build
burp
swallow
yodel
sweep
bounce
walk

Awesome Astronaut

Watch out for the craters on the moon! Can you find the two pictures that are exactly alike?

Answer on page 278

ZOO CREW

The zoo is home to tons of super cool creatures!
Find the names of these zoo animals in the word
search below. Look up, down, backward, forward,
and diagonally.

Alligator	**Orangutan**
Chimpanzee	**Polar bear**
Elephant	**Rhinoceros**
Giraffe	**Tiger**
Lion	**Zebra**

```
J T U E A C C H S L P P M K
Z F N R D F I F G A O B Z J
L O B A J Y V G C M L H Z U
C E Z I H P L Y T L A E X G
Z H O E S P F I O R R F C J
R H I N O C E R O S B F Z M
P G J M I H A L U N E A G K
C N C D P N K L E V A R N Q
V X C T G A W O X L R I C N
O B M U S C N I H L L G X Z
Q Q T I B M Y Z H T I G E R
X A E L A A D X E B E E M D
N K G K M L B C D E M J G S
V R O T A G I L L A E Q M F
```

Answer on page 278

Sudoku
PUZZLE
POWER

Got lots of brain power? Then try to decode this sudoku. Fill in the empty squares so that each row, column, and square contains the numbers 1–9 only once.

		3	6	7				9
6	8							1
		9			1			8
		4			6	8		7
			8		2			
8		6	3			9		
9			1			5		
5							7	4
2				5	3	1		

Design Your Own

TV SHOW

Think about your favorite TV shows. Wouldn't it be cool if the best characters from each show crossed over? Here's your chance to create a TV show!

TV FACTS

Are you a TV nut or just a casual viewer? Improve your knowledge of TV with these fun facts!

The world's oldest TV station started up in 1928. But the broadcasts weren't anything like we see today. Because engineers were still testing the technology, the station only "played" images of a stuffed cat spinning on a turntable for two years!

Think reality TV is a new thing? It's existed since the 1940s in the form of prank shows and talent searches.

The "laugh track" is the audience laughter you can hear during most sitcoms. It's totally fake! Specialized engineers spend hours editing together a laugh track, and can even choose the volume, gender, and quality of the laughs!

Blast Off Maze

Follow the correct path through the maze to get the astronaut to Mars. What's the correct path, you ask? It's the one that is made up of rockets only!

START

FINISH

Answer on page 279

Build It Up!

Solve this rebus puzzle to discover the name of a site where buildings are made.

 – W + N +

– OP + R + ⬆ – P + C +

 – V + – L

Football TERMS

Before you grab the old pigskin or settle in to watch the game, make sure you know your stuff. Here are some important football terms and their meanings.

Backfield: This is the area of the field behind the line of scrimmage.

Blitz: This is a defensive move where the linebackers (who usually stay behind the line of scrimmage) rush into the other team's backfield.

Complete Pass: When a player passes the ball to a teammate, who catches it in the air, it is considered a complete pass.

Down: A down is a unit of the game that starts with a snap or a free kick, and ends when the ball becomes dead (if it is dropped, etc.). There are four downs and during each one the offensive team has a chance to gain ten yards.

End Zone: This is the area between the end line and the goal line. The bounds of the end line are the sidelines.

Field Goal: A field goal earns a team three points and happens when the ball is kicked between the uprights, and above the crossbar, on the goalpost.

Goal Line: The goal line is the front of the end zone. This line goes across the width of the field.

Incomplete Pass: A pass is incomplete if the ball hits the ground before it is caught.

Interception: An interception is when a member of the opposing team catches the ball.

Lines of Scrimmage: Two imaginary lines that extend across the field, parallel to the goal lines.

Offside: Each team is supposed to be behind their own side of the restraining line before the ball is snapped. If any part of a player's body goes beyond that line, he is offside.

Punt: A punt is when the ball is dropped, then kicked before it hits the ground.

Quarterback: The quarterback heads the team's offense.

Sack: A sack happens when the quarterback is tackled behind his line of scrimmage.

Touchdown: A touchdown is worth six points and is awarded when a player crosses the other team's goal line with the ball or catches a pass in their opponent's end zone, or picks up a loose ball in their opponent's end zone.

FOOTBALL FUN

Find these things that have to do with football in the word search below. Look up, down, backward, forward, and diagonally.

Astroturf	End zone	Huddle	Playbook	Stadium
Blitz	Goalpost	Penalty	Quarterback	Touchdown

```
P Z D Z X T H N Z O K T P G
E Y B H S B O S O C N L I O
J Q N W I B L U A P A T E A
E N O Z D N E B C Y A L E L
A C R I D W R B B H D I C P
R X F L N E Y O U D D L G O
F V A S T R O T U R F O D S
W G D R M K I H L P U V W T
T Z A V U I O U W A U S D N
Q U Q B I O Z T J Y N I O R
Q B B L D B V G P M M E Y T
U J Z P A B L I T Z I P P Z
D N B T T I P B M F W O A Y
G E F H S O H X L T G V T V
```

Answer on page 279

Design Your
WHAT'S ON YOUR MIND

What do you think each of these warriors is thinking as he prepares for battle? Fill out the thought bubbles above their heads!

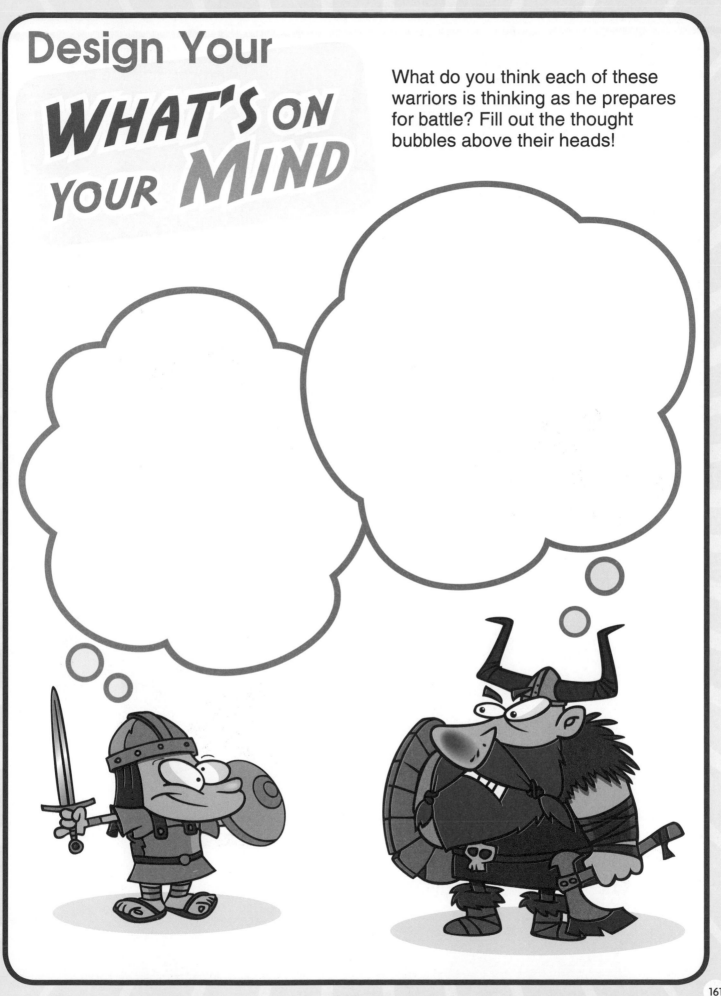

Roller Coaster

Yahoo! Can you find the two pictures that are exactly alike?

Answer on page 280

UNDER THE BIG TOP

Use the clues below to complete this crossword puzzle about the circus.

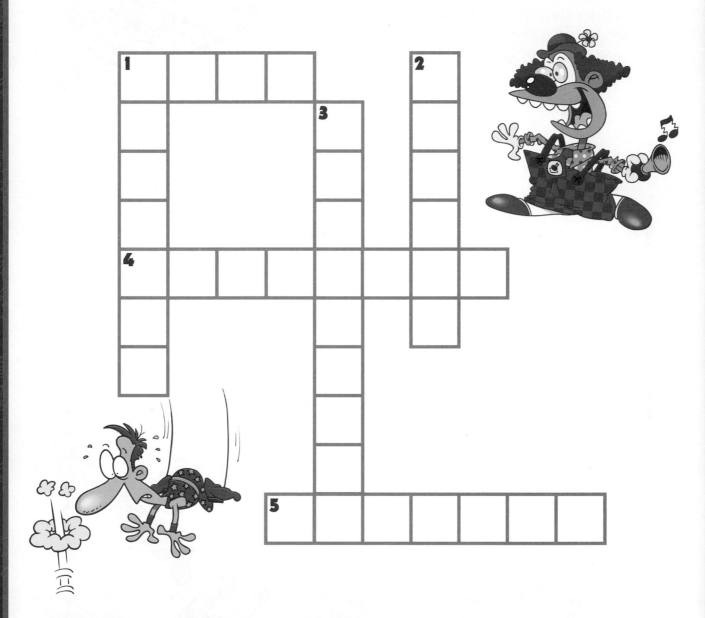

ACROSS
1. Also known as the "Big Top"
4. A really big animal
5. Elephants eat these

DOWN
1. Acrobats swing from these
2. These performers have colorful clothes and big noses.
3. People walk across this, if they can balance.

Sudoku
ROCKING NUMBERS

Try to decode this sudoku. Fill in the empty squares so that each row, column, and square contains the numbers 1–9 only once.

6		9		1		2	3	
8		3	2					
1	4				3	6		8
5	8				6			1
	6	8	4	1	7			
	1	7	3				4	2
7			6			8	1	9
	6				2	4		3
	8		9			5		6

Answer on page 280

Would You Rather...

Which would you rather do?
Look at each pair of options. Think
about them and check the things you
would like best. Ask your friends, too!

Would you rather live...

☐ **On the moon** or ☐ **On Mars?**

Would you rather swim...

☐ **With sharks** or ☐ **With whales?**

Would you rather have...

☐ **An elephant's trunk** or ☐ **A giraffe's neck?**

Would you rather have dinner with...

☐ **Your friend** or ☐ **Your teacher?**

Are you a super seeker? Put your eyes to the test and see if you can find 10 differences between the picture on the top and the one on the bottom.

Answer on page 280

CREEPY CRAWLERS

Use the clues to complete the crossword puzzle about types of bugs.

ACROSS
1. Digs a good picnic
3. Has eight legs
5. Has many, many legs
6. Has yellow and black stripes

DOWN
2. A hairy kind of spider
4. This type of worm sucks blood.

January

Fill in your calendar with all of the January birthdays you don't want to forget.

1	2	3	4	5	6	7
8	9	10	11	12	13	14
15	16	17	18	19	20	21
22	23	24	25	26	27	28
29	30	31				

TO DO:

_____

_____

_____

February

Fill in your calendar with all of the February birthdays you don't want to forget.

1	2	3	4	5	6	7
8	9	10	11	12	13	14
15	16	17	18	19	20	21
22	23	24	25	26	27	28

29

Leap Day!

TO DO:

_____

_____

_____

March

Fill in your calendar with all of the March birthdays you don't want to forget.

1	2	3	4	5	6	7
8	9	10	11	12	13	14
15	16	17	18	19	20	21
22	23	24	25	26	27	28
29	30	31				

TO DO:

_____

_____

_____

April

Fill in your calendar with all of the April birthdays you don't want to forget.

1	2	3	4	5	6	7
8	9	10	11	12	13	14
15	16	17	18	19	20	21
22	23	24	25	26	27	28
29	30					

TO DO:

_____

_____

_____

May

Fill in your calendar with all of the May birthdays you don't want to forget.

1	2	3	4	5	6	7
8	9	10	11	12	13	14
15	16	17	18	19	20	21
22	23	24	25	26	27	28
29	30	31				

TO DO:

_____
_____
_____

June

Fill in your calendar with all of the June birthdays you don't want to forget.

1	2	3	4	5	6	7
8	9	10	11	12	13	14
15	16	17	18	19	20	21
22	23	24	25	26	27	28
29	30					

TO DO:

_____

_____

_____

July

Fill in your calendar with all of the July birthdays you don't want to forget.

1	2	3	4	5	6	7
8	9	10	11	12	13	14
15	16	17	18	19	20	21
22	23	24	25	26	27	28
29	30	31				

TO DO:

_____

_____

_____

August

Fill in your calendar with all of the August birthdays you don't want to forget.

1	2	3	4	5	6	7
8	9	10	11	12	13	14
15	16	17	18	19	20	21
22	23	24	25	26	27	28
29	30	31				

TO DO:

_____

_____

_____

September

Fill in your calendar with all of the September birthdays you don't want to forget.

1	2	3	4	5	6	7
8	9	10	11	12	13	14
15	16	17	18	19	20	21
22	23	24	25	26	27	28
29	30					

TO DO:

_____

_____

_____

October

Fill in your calendar with all of the October birthdays you don't want to forget.

1	2	3	4	5	6	7
8	9	10	11	12	13	14
15	16	17	18	19	20	21
22	23	24	25	26	27	28
29	30	31				

TO DO:

_____

_____

_____

November

Fill in your calendar with all of the November birthdays you don't want to forget.

1	2	3	4	5	6	7
8	9	10	11	12	13	14
15	16	17	18	19	20	21
22	23	24	25	26	27	28
29	30					

TO DO:
_____
_____
_____

December

Fill in your calendar with all of the December birthdays you don't want to forget.

1	2	3	4	5	6	7
8	9	10	11	12	13	14
15	16	17	18	19	20	21
22	23	24	25	26	27	28
29	30	31				

TO DO:

_____

_____

_____

Sudoku
SMART MATH

Use your math skills and try to decode this sudoku. Fill in the empty squares so that each row, column, and square contains the numbers 1–9 only once.

	8	4	6		5	7		9
				8				4
			2				3	
				9		6	7	
7			3	5	6			8
	6	5		4				
	1				3			
5								
2		8	9		1	5	4	

Solve this rebus puzzle to discover the name of something you would find in a park.

___ ___ ___ ___ ___ ___ ___

___ ___ ___ ___ ___

Making WORDS

PINEWOOD DERBY

_____   _____

_____   _____

_____   _____

_____   _____

_____   _____

_____   _____

_____   _____

_____   _____

_____   _____

Design Your THOUGHT PROCESS

What is this muddy guy thinking? Fill out the thought bubble above his head.

Cool Cowboy

Let's ride! Can you find the two pictures that are exactly alike?

Answer on page 282

Making Invisible Ink

How To TIPS

This is a super-cool way to get secret messages to your pals! With invisible ink, no one will know what you are saying, unless you want them to. Be sure to ask an adult for help and supervision.

MATERIALS

- **1 Lemon**
- **Paintbrush**
- **White paper**

DIRECTIONS

- Squeeze the lemon over a bowl to collect the lemon juice.

- Dip the paintbrush in the lemon juice and write a secret message on the paper.

- Once it is dry, bake your piece of paper at 325 degrees for three to five minutes.

- Take it out of oven and read it.

HOW DOES IT WORKS?

The heat burns the lemon juice, making it reappear on the paper.

Let's Draw a
Tyrannosaurus

On a separate piece of paper, follow these simple steps using a pencil and an eraser.

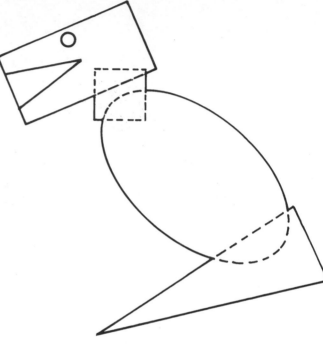

1 Use rectangles, ovals, squares, and triangles for the basic body, head, and tail. These are only guidelines, so draw them lightly.

2 Using basic shapes as your guide, add small forearms and large legs, as shown.

3 Use your guidelines to form a clean outline of the basic body shape. As you work, erase any lines you don't need.

4 Put all the finishing touches on your drawing. Give Tyrannosaurus a ferocious look, big teeth, a mean look in its eye, and lots of skin effects.

PARKS AND RECREATION

Where do you like to hang when school's out? Find the names of these awesomely fun places in the word search below. Look up, down, backward, forward, and diagonally.

Aquarium

Beach

Campsite

Hiking trail

Lodge

Museum

Park

Ski slopes

Summer camp

Zoo

```
A H L F K Z L K B Z S H R T
Q K O K D C I J R I S Z R B
U T D O F S A C C A U H W H
A J G A F H R M A C P D Q D
R A E U Y A N U M V Q P M P
I H K Z N T G I P S M O M R
U H C A E B N S S D I A B M
M M O F S A I E I M C T U P
P G E B W Z K X T R L S E N
S R O B V N I N E E E V R Y
O X C Y W W H M Z U S Z V A
O S S H Y B M F M I P U H K
Z M I Z Z U X Q L R V Z M D
Q S K I S L O P E S D V M A
```

Answer on page 282

Create Your COOLEST GUYS EVER LIST

Who are your favorite people to hang out with at school, at home, at the skate park—or anywhere, for that matter? Make a list of your closest buddies.

The Coolest Friends Ever:

_____   _____
_____   _____
_____   _____
_____   _____
_____   _____
_____   _____
_____   _____
_____   _____

List Your Time Warp

Ever wonder what it must have been like to live in the past? What do you think you would have liked best about each of these eras?

The 1800s:

The 1970s:

The 1920s:

The 1980s:

The 1960s:

The 1990s:

YESTERDAY

TOMORROW

Would You Rather...

Which would you rather do?
Look at each pair of options. Think about them and check the things you would like best. Ask your friends, too!

Would you rather go...

☐ Skydiving   or   ☐ Camping?

Would you rather be...

☐ Playing video games   or   ☐ Reading a book

Would you rather go...

☐ Ice skating   or   ☐ Skiing?

Would you rather be in a...

☐ Food fight   or   ☐ Water-balloon fight?

Making WORDS

Let's scramble some letters. Can you make 15 or more words of five or more letters from the following phrase?

WATER-BALLOON FIGHT

Answer on page 282

Write Your

Pretend you're a dragon slayer! What's a typical day like for you? Write a blog entry about it here!

Once Upon a Time...

Caption your picture _____

_____

_____

_____

_____

_____

_____

_____

_____

_____

_____

post by_____ time _____

Sudoku
STRAIGHT UP!

Try to decode this sudoku. Fill in the empty squares so that each row, column, and square contains the numbers 1–9 only once.

	2		5		7			
	5		9		6			
1				8			3	7
	1	4			5	8		
	7							1
		2	1			6	9	
2	3			9				1
			2		3		8	
			7		1		2	

Water Park

Cowabunga, dude! Can you find the two pictures that are exactly alike?

Answer on page 283

Pool Maze

Follow the correct path through the maze to get the kid to the pool. What's the correct path, you ask? It's the one that is made up of life preservers only.

START

FINISH

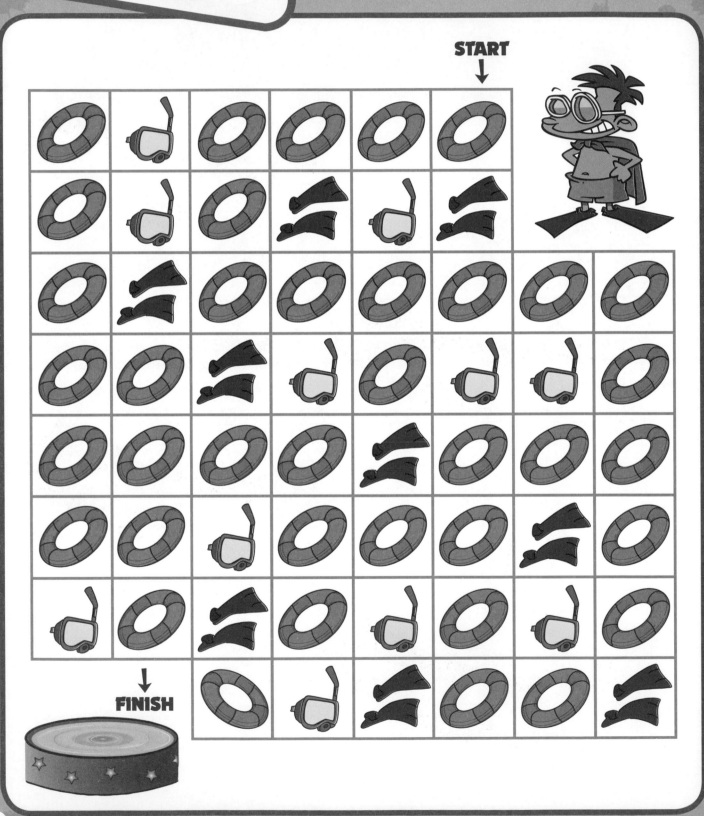

Answer on page 283

MASKED BALL

Search, find, and circle these 10 things.

BASEBALL BAT
DRUM
ELECTRIC FAN

HORSESHOE
PAINTBRUSH
SANDWICH
SCISSORS

SNAKE
STARFISH
TRASH CAN

Answer on page 283

Would You Rather...

Which would you rather do? Look at each pair of options. Think about them and check the things you would like best. Ask your friends, too!

Would you rather have...

☐ 100 so-so friends   or   ☐ 2 REALLY great friends?

Would you rather have...

☐ A missing finger   or   ☐ An extra toe?

Would you rather...

☐ Play sports   or   ☐ Coach sports?

Would you rather go...

☐ Skydiving   or   ☐ Bungee jumping?

Create Your
SILLY
CONVERSATION

This monster just got himself a new puppy! What do you think the monster thinks of his new pet? And what do you think the puppy thinks about being adopted by a monster? Fill in their thoughts in the speech bubbles!

The Great Outdoors

Are you a super seeker? Put your eyes to the test and see if you can find 10 differences between the picture on the top and the one on the bottom.

Answer on page 283

SUMMER CAMP

Use the clues about summer camp to solve the crossword puzzle.

ACROSS
4. Helps you cook things when you're out in the wilderness
5. You can float on the water in this
7. You might sleep in this
8. An adult who works at the camp

DOWN
1. You toast this over a campfire
2. Tell this kind of story around a fire to spook the campers
3. Holds your water
6. Paddle this by yourself or with another person

Ban Bullying
How To TIPS //

Bullying is no joke and it should be taken seriously. Here are some tips to help you cope.

What To Do If You Are BEING BULLIED

- Tell an adult, like a teacher or a parent.
- Ask your friends to stand by you and help.
- Choose your words carefully, so that you can defend yourself.
- Stay calm and confident.
- Ignore the bully and walk away. Fighting back will only make the problem worse.

Remember: Lots of kids encounter some form of bullying. You are not alone. No one deserves to be bullied.

What To Do If You WITNESS BULLYING

- Speak up on behalf of the person being bullied.
- Ask the bully to stop.
- Comfort the person being bullied and offer friendship and a shoulder to lean on.
- Walk away and get help.
- Find an adult who can help the situation.

What To Do If You ARE THE BULLY

- Talk to someone you trust and get advice on how to get along better with others.
- Apologize to the kids you have bullied.
- Before you bully, think about whether your words will help or hurt another student.
- Don't bully because you are pressured into doing so. No one likes a bully.

TYPES OF CLOTHES

Find these types of clothes in the word search below. Look up, down, backward, forward, and diagonally.

| Hat | Jeans | Pajamas | Shoes | Socks |
| Jacket | Necktie | Shirt | Shorts | Trousers |

```
V C A V P T S H O R T S S S
R T L S E K E J J A N L A H
A K E K A J B I H R R L M M
K R C F G E L W T Q Z B A Y
J A R G M O R S I K M B J W
J E S R E S U O R T C S A P
B T A G Q M B C M L H E P W
Y G A N K R U K X O X X N W
T R I H S S U S E Q X D F N
D H K G I T E S S P X W H O
Y K K R R B X Z Q V B O E W
I S T A I R M K R D R J P L
W L G U D B S T G V B A U R
Q K R W N G S N R S U C S S
```

Answer on page 284

Design Your
ULTIMATE T-SHIRT

Do you have a favorite band or a retro graphic that you'd love to sport on a t-shirt? Design it here!

MY PET DINO

Fill in the blanks to complete this silly story about what it might be like to have a pet dinosaur. Pick a NOUN, ADJECTIVE, or VERB from the word bank to place in a corresponding blank, or think of your own wacky words!

I've been begging my parents forever to let me get a pet dinosaur,

and they finally agreed! My dinosaur is _____ and a little bit
[ADJECTIVE]

_____ and he loves to _____ all day long! My sister likes
[ADJECTIVE]   [VERB]

to _____ right along with him. The only problem is that he keeps
[VERB]

chewing up my _____ and _____. One day I caught
[NOUN]   [NOUN]

my dinosaur about to_____ the _____!
[VERB]   [NOUN]

WORD BANK

ADJECTIVES

wooly
itchy   weak
silly   dumb
scared   sweet
gentle   brave

NOUNS

watermelon   computer
baseball cap cereal
football   t-shirt
homework   bed
sweater

VERBS

chomp
jump   read
jog   ride
nap   bow
sew   sit

206

Create Your
THINGS THAT GO LIST

How many vehicles—of any kind—can you think of? Set a timer for two minutes. Then, see how many vehicles you can name in that time! Test your friends, too.

Cat Maze

Follow the correct path through the maze to get the cat to the mouse. What's the correct path, you ask? It's the one that is made up of balls of yarn only.

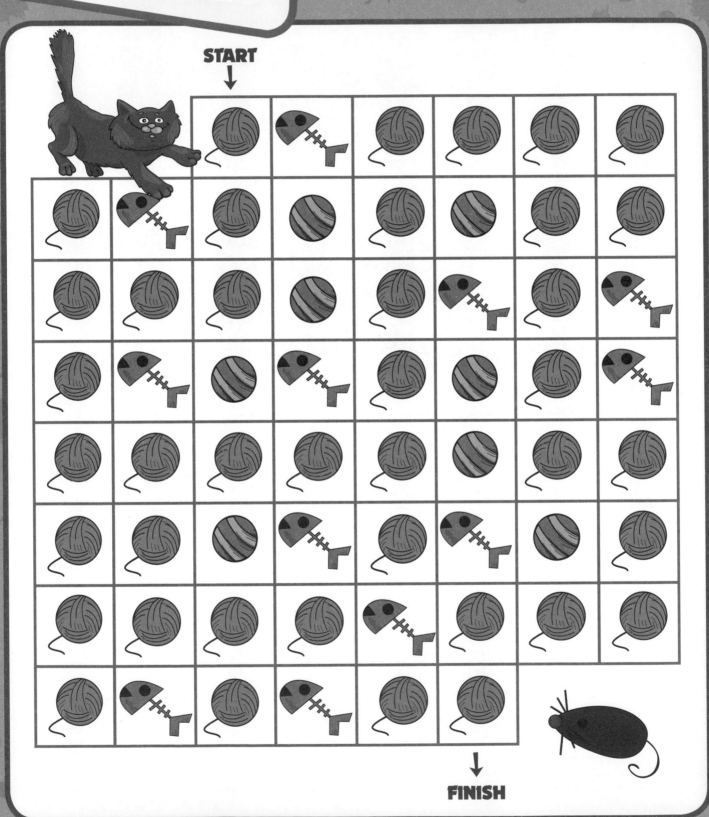

START

FINISH

Answer on page 284

Speedy Train

All aboard! Can you find the two pictures that are exactly alike?

Answer on page 284

Let's Draw a
Minotaur

On a separate piece of paper, follow these simple steps using a pencil and an eraser.

1 Begin with a circle for the head and add more circular shapes for the body, legs, and feet.

2 Add horns to both sides of the head, arms, and hands. Draw the split in the hooves on the feet.

3 Add straps on the arms and a loincloth. Erase any unwanted guidelines.

4 Finalize the drawing by adding the axe, belt details, and armbands. Complete with color and shading.

LET'S PARTY!

Get your party on! Find the names of these things that have to do with parties in the word search below. Look up, down, backward, forward, and diagonally.

Balloons	Cake	Candy	Friends	Holiday
Birthday	Candles	Costume	Gifts	Sleepover

```
Z S S S S V V O G A A B Y C
I H X L E G X L U U I W A V
D O Q E L Y B L I R C K A K
D Q S E D O W Z T L E O T F
J C M P N Z H H B S G R K L
W S U O A Y D H O L I D A Y
V Y A V C A S N O O L L A B
E T E E Y D G V A D Y S Z Q
N M C R N U T I B A M F H X
K D U E P F F S F C Z C E C
J D I T A H E B P T P A H U
G R F A S D A Z O Y S N J P
F V D D T O L J M V A D K M
U Q M Q B Q C D X B S Y Z P
```

Answer on page 285

Sudoku
WHAT'S YOUR IQ?

Try to decode this sudoku. Fill in the empty squares so that each row, column, and square contains the numbers 1–9 only once.

	7				2			
		1		6	9	7		5
					7	8	6	9
					1			6
	5		6		3		7	
8		2	9					
4	2	7	3					
9		6	2	4		3		
			7				4	

Answer on page 285

Design Your Own
RACE CAR COMPETITION

On your mark, get set, finish this racetrack! Draw in the rest of the track, the cars, and the crowd!

FOOD FIGHT!

Fill in the blanks to complete this silly story about what might happen in a food fight. Pick a NOUN, ADJECTIVE, or VERB from the word bank to place in a corresponding blank, or think of your own wacky words!

It was a normal day in the school cafeteria. That is, until my friend

threw a _____ and a _____ across the room! It _____ed
         [NOUN]   [NOUN]   [VERB]

the _____ and totally made a _____ sound. Some
      [NOUN]   [ADJECTIVE]

people felt completely _____ and others got into it. It was
                          [ADJECTIVE]

so _____! The worst thing that was _____ed in the food
     [ADJECTIVE]   [VERB]

fight was definitely the _____, because it _____ed all over
                            [NOUN]   [VERB]

the _____!
      [NOUN]

WORD BANK

ADJECTIVES
gross
stinky
squishy
slimy
neat
weird
squiggly
yellow
hot

NOUNS
pretzel
yogurt
pickle
spider
book
cheese
skirt
toilet
baseball bat

VERBS
squish
leap
yell
soar
sniff
jump
slurp
yawn
bump

Old West

Are you a super seeker? Put your eyes to the test and see if you can find 10 differences between the picture on the top and the one on the bottom.

Answer on page 285

Pirate TERMS

Ahoy: What you yell when you want to attract someone's attention, sort of like "hey!".

Arrr!: An exclamation.

Aye: Yes.

Black Spot: A black spot is left on something by a pirate to indicate a threat to his enemy.

Blimey!: An exclamation a pirate uses to express surprise.

Davy Jones' Locker: Davy Jones was a famous pirate who supposedly sank every ship he took over. Davy Jones' locker is a made-up place at the bottom of the ocean. When your ship is sunk and you die in the sea, you are said to have been sent to Davy Jones' locker.

Fire in the Hole: This is the warning that is shouted before a cannon is fired.

Handsomely: This means to do something quickly or correctly.

Ho: This expression is used to indicate that you have spotted something ahead, such as, "Land, ho!"

Hornswaggle: Cheat.

Marooned: To be stranded. Usually used when one is stranded on an island.

Me: My.

Mutiny: An uprising against the person in charge (usually the captain of the ship).

Pillage: To rob someone.

Piracy: A robbery committed at sea is piracy.

Plunder: Another word for pillage.

Run a Shot Across the Bow: This is what you say when you want one of your mates to fire a warning shot.

Sea Legs: To be able to adjust to the motion of being on a ship at sea.

Shiver Me Timbers!: A pirate says this when he is totally shocked by something.

Swab: To clean the deck of a ship.

Walk the Plank: When a pirate takes over a ship, he will tell the pirates already on board to walk the plank, meaning, they have to walk the plank, into the water, and give up their ship.

Ye: You.

SHIVER ME TIMBERS!

Use the clues about pirates to solve the crossword puzzle.

ACROSS
1. Pirates wear this on an eye
4. Another word for "my"
6. Sometimes pirates will give other pirates this type of "dot"
7. Weapon commonly used by pirates for defense
8. What pirates say when they see land
9. A pirate's main vehicle of transportation

DOWN
2. Means "yes"
3. This is shot out of a cannon
5. Some pirates have these in their ears

Answer on page 285

Create Your
SUPER HEROES LIST

Who are some of your heroes—the people you admire the most? It can be anybody, real or not. List why each person is a hero to you.

My Heroes:

_____   _____

_____   _____

_____   _____

_____   _____

_____   _____

_____   _____

_____   _____

_____   _____

Space FACTS

The asteroid belt is a strip of asteroids, or rocks, floating around the solar system. The belt is made up of material that didn't make it into the planets during the formation of the solar system—the asteroids were too close to Jupiter's strong pull of gravity and were led away from all other planets.

A probe called Luna 1 was launched in 1959 by the Soviet Union. It was supposed to land on the moon and collect soil samples, but it missed its destination and has since been lost in space.

The sun's surface is constantly releasing jets of gas, known as solar flares. These flares can react with Earth's atmosphere to create dazzling colors—in the northern hemisphere; this is called the Northern Lights, or Aurora Borealis.

Constellation Creation

Using the stars on this page, draw lines to form as many constellations as you know!

Underwater Swimmer

Solve this rebus puzzle to discover the name of something swimmers should look out for.

S + 🎵(harp) - P + K 🦇(bat)

- B + T + 🃏(cards) - J

_ _ _ _ _ _ _ _

_ _ _ _ _ _ _ _

Monster Maze

Even monsters hate bad weather. Follow the path made up from numbers **1** through **25** to help the monster get to the house.

Start →

1	2	3	4	19	5	2
2	8	7	5	6	4	3
3	12	13	6	7	8	9
4	5	7	8	9	10	11
1	6				24	23
3	7		**Finish ←**		25	24
9	8				3	23
10	20				2	22
11	3	18	16	12	18	21
12	13	14	15	10	6	20
20	21	15	16	17	18	19
19	18	17	16	15	14	13

Answer on page 286

Crime Fighter

Are you a super seeker? Put your eyes to the test and see if you can find 10 differences between the picture on the top and the one on the bottom.

Answer on page 286

CAMPING

Pack up your gear and get ready for some campfire craziness! Find the names of these camping terms in the word search below. Look up, down, backward, forward, and diagonally.

Backpack
Cabin
Campfire   **Fishing**   **Sleeping bag**   **Tent**
Campground   **Ghost stories**   **S'mores**   **Woods**

```
C M T O I Y C K O N B G E W
D O Z H W R C Y Y W H G R N
N W R C T A O T J O P P I G
G S V D P F S H S O Z J F R
U S M K N T B T A D C O P W
B R C O C U S X A S H F M X
M A V A R T O T N E T D A V
B R B K O E A R Q E M H C O
M I O R G E S G G T M N R O
N C I G A B G N I P E E L S
O E F I S H I N G B M C T Z
S U G P Z L I K R F X A I H
M W K E S V U M R O X N C U
Y Z D S X U M J A T A W D L
```

Answer on page 286

Design Your Own
SCUBA ADVENTURE

Fill the ocean with sea creatures for this scuba diver to encounter. The weirder, the better! What kind of things would you want to see on a scuba trip?

Let's Draw an
Aston Martin

On a separate piece of paper, follow these simple steps using a pencil and an eraser.

1 Begin by sketching the basic shapes of the body. Draw through your shapes to establish form. Then draw two tires.

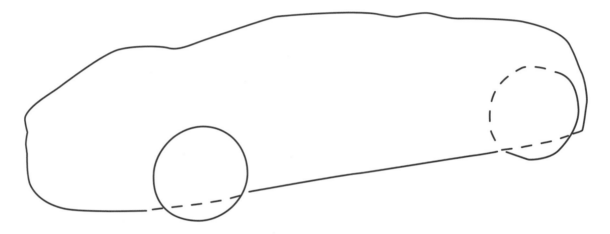

2 Erase the unwanted lines near the tires. Add more detail with shapes of the grille, lights, windows, and door. Draw wheel wells.

3 Continue by adding more detail with crisp clean lines. Add mirrors and cockpit details. Draw the cool rims and use lines to show form on the hood and side panel.

4 Choose a gold color for your Aston Martin and black for the interior. Show shadows and reflections with a darker tone, and add highlights with lighter tones. Finish off the rims and hit the road!

Would You Rather...

Which would you rather do?
Look at each pair of options. Think
about them and check the things you
would like best. Ask your friends, too!

Would you rather watch...

☐ **Comedians**   **or**   ☐ **Cartoons?**

Would you rather smell...

☐ **Pie**   **or**   ☐ **Beef jerky?**

Would you rather...

☐ **Snort milk out of your nose**   **or**   ☐ **Burp?**

Would you rather have...

☐ **Freckles**   **or**   ☐ **A tan?**

Tie a Tie!
How To
TIPS

//////////////////////////

You might not be bombarded with invitations for fancy parties right now, but learning how to tie a tie is essential for any dude's future. Practice!

Steps

1. Drape the tie around your neck, so that the ends rest on your chest.

2. The wide end of the tie should be on your right and the other end should be on your left.

3. Cross the wide end over the other end.

4. Now bring the wide end underneath the narrow end from left to right.

5. Next, pull the wide end over from right to left.

6. Put the wide end under the knot.

7. Bring the wide end down and pass the loop in front. Make sure that the knot is tightened.

8. Pull the narrow end down gently and, at the same time, move the knot up until it reaches the center of the collar.

Create Your
FOOTBALL STRATEGY

It's time for football season! You've just been hired as the main coach of the best football team in the country. Draw one of your team's signature plays.

TOUCHDOWN

-10 -20 -30 -40

-10 -20 -30 -40

-40- -30- -20- -10-

TOUCHDOWN

40- 30- 20- 10-

Wet Weather

Solve this rebus puzzle to discover the name of something that makes an appearance in wet weather.

_ _ _ _ _ _ _ _ _ _ _

Create Your
FAVE JUNK
FOOD LIST

If junk food was healthy and you could eat as much of it as you wanted, what would you choose? Make a list of your favorite junk foods.

My Favorite Junk Foods:

_____   _____

_____   _____

_____   _____

_____   _____

_____   _____

_____   _____

_____   _____

_____   _____

_____   _____

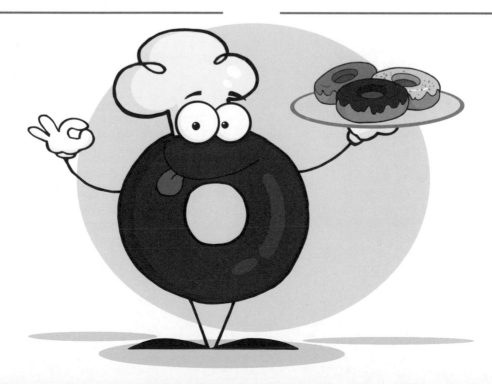

Road Trip

Are you a super seeker? Put your eyes to the test and see if you can find 10 differences between the picture on the top and the one on the bottom.

Answer on page 287

Car Talk
How To TIPS

Need to know what a spark plug does? The answer to that and other engine questions are right here!

Engine

The engine converts energy into useful mechanical motion. It burns fuel to create heat and then propel the car.

Spark Plug

The spark plug makes the spark that ignites the air/fuel mixture so that combustion happens. This has to happen at the right moment for everything to work correctly.

Cylinder

The core of the engine; the part the holds the pistons.

Piston

A piston is a piece of metal that moves up and down to help change gas into energy.

Valves

The valves open at the right time to let in air and fuel and to let out exhaust.

Let's Draw a

Formula One Racecar

On a separate piece of paper, follow these simple steps using a pencil and an eraser.

1 Draw the basic body shape and the shape of the spoiler. Include the tire shapes and draw through to make sure they are correct.

2 Erase any extra lines. Draw the driver's seat, wheel wells, lights, and interesting aerodynamic shapes on the sides. Connect the spoiler to the body of the car.

3 Draw mirrors, rims, air intakes, and other details. Add a number to the hood.

4 A silver and red color combination is a great choice for this car. Make sure you blend the red into the silver for an extra-cool look. This car is ready to win the race!

Decode-a- RIDDLE

Write the letter that comes THREE LETTERS AFTER each letter shown below to decode and solve the riddle.

T E X Q   T L R I A   V L R

D B Q   F C   B S B O V

X R Q L J L Y F I B

L K   Q E B   O L X A

T X P   M F K H **?**

X   M F K H

-

Z X O   K X Q F L K

242   **Answer on page 287**

INTO THE WOODS

Search, find, and circle these 10 things.

ALARM CLOCK   **CHICKEN DRUMSTICK**   **LOCK**

BIGFOOT   **FISHBOWL**   **RULER**

BOW TIE   **FORK**   **TREE ORNAMENT**

ICE SKATES (2)

Answer on page 287

Design Your Own
WHAT'S IN A NAME?

Wonder what it would be like if you had a different name? Here's your chance to try out some new names. List them!

Possible New Names:

_____   _____
_____   _____
_____   _____
_____   _____
_____   _____
_____   _____
_____   _____
_____   _____

Sudoku
SUPER SOLVER

Try to decode this sudoku. Fill in the empty squares so that each row, column, and square contains the numbers 1–9 only once.

4		2	5	7				1
			2				7	
				1	4	3	5	
	1	4				8		
	3						6	
		9				7	1	
	6	1	9	3				
	4				5			
2				4	1	5		6

LOST in the LIBRARY

Fill in the blanks to complete this silly story about what it might be like to be lost in a gigantic library. Pick a NOUN, ADJECTIVE, or VERB from the word bank to place in a corresponding blank, or think of your own wacky words!

I was reading a book in a quiet corner and I got locked in the library at night.

I was in the _____ section when I completely forgot to _____. I
        [NOUN]   **[VERB]**

was so _____ that I decided to _____ right away! Before I knew
        [ADJECTIVE]   **[VERB]**

it, a _____ approached and told me to _____! The library turns
        [NOUN]   **[VERB]**

into a _____ and _____ place during the night.
        [ADJECTIVE]   **[ADJECTIVE]**

WORD BANK

ADJECTIVES

scary
short
purple
thick
loud

smart
squiggly
cool
hot

NOUNS

magazine
computer
machine
guard
present

truck
dust ball
toilet
hot dog

VERBS

leap
scream
drop
free fall
sleep

sing
slurp
blow
spit

Pool Party

Are you a super seeker? Put your eyes to the test and see if you can find 10 differences between the picture on the top and the one on the bottom.

Answer on page 288

Design Your Own
SLIMY SUNDAE

Turn this ice-cream sundae into the grossest, smelliest, most heinous sundae in history! Add worms, ants, tar—whatever you think will make it the grossest!

Winter Wonderland

Solve this rebus puzzle to discover the name of something that strikes in the dead of winter.

Would You Rather...

Which would you rather do?
Look at each pair of options. Think about them and check the things you would like best. Ask your friends, too!

Would you rather have...

☐ The ability to fly   or   ☐ The ability to be invisible?

Would you rather eat...

☐ 25 hot dogs   or   ☐ 25 hamburgers?

Would you rather be...

☐ Really, really tall   or   ☐ Really, really short?

Would you rather eat...

☐ A tarantula   or   ☐ A cricket?

School Maze

Follow the correct path through the maze to get the boy to his locker. What's the correct path, you ask? It's the one that is made up of backpacks only!

START

FINISH

How To
TIPS

Do you devour crime shows and reality cop shows? Do you dream of taking down a perp? Find out all you need to know about fingerprints right here!

HOW TO
FINGERPRINT A PERP

- Shade in an area of paper with the point of a pencil.
- Rub your finger into the spot.
- Stick the sticky side of a piece of tape on the finger.
- Tape that to a clean piece of white paper.
- Label it.
- Repeat the process with all of the fingers.
- An alternative, messier method: press each fingertip into an inkpad.

DUSTING FOR PRINTS

Stuff You will need:
- Drinking glass
- Cocoa powder
- Small soft brush
- Transparent tape
- Five sheets of light-colored paper

1. Press your finger on the side of a drinking glass. Tip: Sticky or oily fingers make better prints.
2. Coat the prints with a dusting of cocoa powder.
3. Brush gently on the glass. The excess powder will disappear, but the fingerprints will remain.
4. Place the sticky side of the tape on the dusted fingerprint. Then tape it to the paper.
5. If you're dusting for prints on a dark surface, use baby powder instead of cocoa powder.

TRY OUT YOUR FINGERPRINTS HERE:

Design Your Own

DESTINATION: WEIRD!

This is the hottest new design in vacation resorts! It's a little odd… but that's what gives it its charm! Can you come up with a list of possible names for this unique new style of architecture?

WHAT STINKS?

Fill in the blanks to complete this silly story about something colossally smelly. Pick a NOUN, ADJECTIVE, or VERB from the word bank to place in a corresponding blank, or think of your own wacky words!

Woooooo, that is some stinky smell! I left a _____ in my _____
[NOUN]   [NOUN]

and totally forgot all about it. Then, I smelled a _____ odor. It
[ADJECTIVE]

made me completely _____ and the dude with the locker next
[ADJECTIVE]

to mine was going to _____ when he whiffed it. Then I went to
[VERB]

_____ it right away—let's hope the _____ is gone!
[VERB]   [NOUN]

WORD BANK

ADJECTIVES

smelly
gross
sweet
nasty
yucky

yummy
sour
crazy
weird

NOUNS

tuna fish
cheese stick
dirty sock
hot dog
salad

pickle
carrot
muffin
scarf

VERBS

puke
gag
spit
faint
laugh

sit
jump
pass out
cough

Let's Draw a
Vampire

On a separate piece of paper, follow these simple steps using a pencil and an eraser.

1 Begin with basic shapes for the head, body, and legs.

2 Add arms, hands, and feet. Create guidelines on the face.

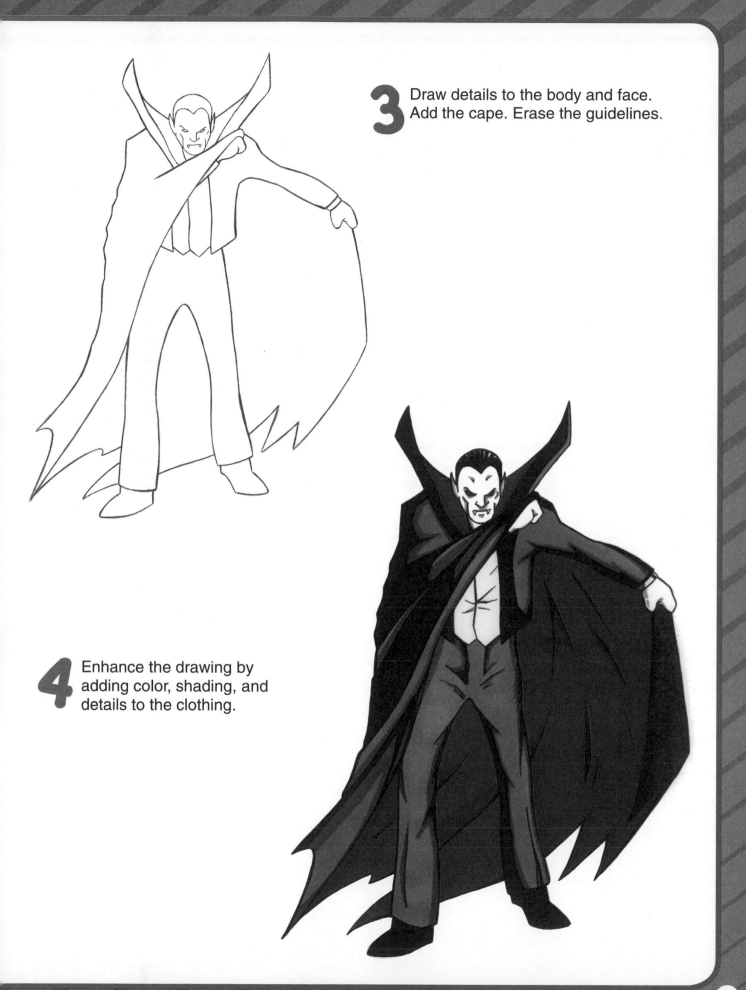

3 Draw details to the body and face. Add the cape. Erase the guidelines.

4 Enhance the drawing by adding color, shading, and details to the clothing.

Design Your Own
WHO'S COMING TO TOWN?

This looks like a quaint little town, doesn't it? Well, a pack of zombies, ghouls, and monsters are about to invade! Do some drawing and depict what the town will look like AFTER the ghoul fest!

Write Your BLOG

If you could invent something, what would it be? What would it do? What would you call it? Write a blog entry about it here!

Invent It!

Caption your picture _____

_____

_____

_____

_____

_____

_____

_____

_____

post by_____ time _____

Answers

Page 4
Construction Maze

Page 5
Brain Builder

1	4	6	7	5	3	9	2	8
2	5	3	4	8	9	7	1	6
9	8	7	1	2	6	5	4	3
6	3	5	2	7	8	1	9	4
7	9	1	3	6	4	2	8	5
4	2	8	9	1	5	6	3	7
5	6	4	8	9	2	3	7	1
3	1	2	5	4	7	8	6	9
8	7	9	6	3	1	4	5	2

Page 6
Tool Time

Drill   **Sander**
Hammer   **Saw**
Level   **Screwdriver**
Nail gun **Trowel**
Pliers   **Wrench**

Page 7
Rockin' Rebus

B A S K E T B A L L

Answers

Page 11
Types of Ice Cream

Across:
- 3. SPLIT
- 4. NEAPOLITAN
- 5. MILKSHAKE
- 7. SUNDAE

Down:
- 1. SHERBET
- 2. STRAWBERRY
- 6. SANDWICH

ACROSS
3. Usually made with bananas
4. A mix of vanilla, chocolate, and strawberry
5. Made with ice cream, milk, and flavored syrup
7. Has a cherry on top

DOWN
1. A fruity ice cream made with only a little milk
2. A popular flavor of fruit ice cream
6. Vanilla between two cookies

Page 13
On The Lake

Anchor Ladder Marina Paddle Radio
Dock Life jacket Outrigger Propeller Sail

Page 14
Scary Dragon

Page 18
Super Smart

3	2	1	5	8	4	6	9	7
7	5	4	6	2	9	1	3	8
6	9	8	7	1	3	4	2	5
8	7	5	9	4	2	3	1	6
9	4	3	1	6	5	7	8	2
1	6	2	8	3	7	5	4	9
2	8	7	3	5	1	9	6	4
5	1	6	4	9	8	2	7	3
4	3	9	2	7	6	8	5	1

Answers

Page 21
Ready for Rebus

M O V I E
T H E A T E R

Page 24
Safari Animals

Page 25
Sundae Maze

Page 27
School Trip

Answers

Page 29
Halloween Maze

Page 32
Super Fan

Page 33
Think Tank

9	3	4	7	6	1	5	8	2
2	8	7	9	3	5	4	6	1
6	1	5	8	4	2	7	9	3
4	9	3	1	2	7	8	5	6
8	6	2	5	9	3	1	7	4
5	7	1	6	8	4	3	2	9
7	4	9	3	5	6	2	1	8
3	5	6	2	1	8	9	4	7
1	2	8	4	7	9	6	3	5

Page 35
Zombie Attack!

Answers

Page 38
Baseball Star

Page 42
Action Figure

ACTION FIGURE

acorn	cure	once
acting	eating	orange
air	face	out
art	factor	rag
aunt	faint	range
auto	fern	ring
café	fig	rut
can	four	tear
cane	great	tie
car	groan	tiger
cite	icon	tiring
corn	ignore	tongue
cougar	ion	tragic
count	nag	train
crate	neat	true
cringe	ogre	tuna

Page 43
Family Portrait

Page 45
Decode-a-Riddle

W H A T   K I N D
T E X Q   H F K A

O F   E A R S   D O
L C   B X O P   A L

T R A I N S   H A V E ?
Q O X F K P   E X S B

E N G I N E E R S
B K D F K B B O P

Answers

Page 46
Video Games

Arcade	Console	Gamer	Keyboard	Role playing
Computer	Controller	Joystick	Programmer	Television

Page 48
Yummy Breakfast!

ACROSS
1. Cooked bread
5. Round, flat, and yummy
6. You usually pour milk over this

DOWN
2. Made with eggs and other ingredients mixed in
3. Some people drink this instead of coffee
4. A meat you eat with eggs

Page 49
Basketball Maze

START ↓

FINISH →

Page 51
Super Skater

266

Answers

Page 54
Creature Feature

Bigfoot Dragon Gnome Mermaid Ogre
Centaur Gargoyle Leprechaun Mummy Vampire

N Y W C X S U R O A F B E S
W U Z Z N F U E G O R A L D
Y Z A Q W A R G A L S O Y E
F M W H T F B A A I Q J O U
Q B M N C V A M P I R E G E
N J E U I E D U D Q X K R S
M C Q Y M R R M G A B B A N
N E K H A V U P I V I E G K
J P R G C U D X E U G R F P
P O O M E M O N G L F G C T
V N B V A X U E O T O O L C
O U E J Q I D Y X R O D Q W
W S R W T Q D S S P T F V Y
H F W Z D Z W J E U B E N M

Page 58
Bouncy Castle

Page 59
Brilliant Brainiac

1	2	7	4	8	9	3	5	6
3	6	8	5	2	7	1	9	4
9	4	5	6	3	1	2	7	8
8	9	3	2	1	5	4	6	7
2	7	4	8	6	3	5	1	9
5	1	6	7	9	4	8	3	2
4	3	2	1	7	6	9	8	5
7	5	9	3	4	8	6	2	1
6	8	1	9	5	2	7	4	3

Page 60
Decode-a-Riddle

1=A	7=G	13=M	19=S	23=W
2=B	8=H	14=N	20=T	24=X
3=C	9=I	15=O	21=U	25=Y
4=D	10=J	16=P	22=V	26=Z
5=E	11=K	17=Q		
6=F	12=L	18=R		

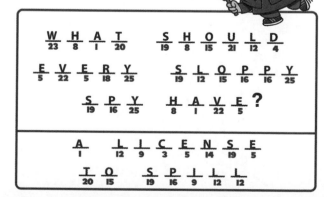

W H A T   S H O U L D
23 8 1 20   19 8 15 21 12 4

E V E R Y   S L O P P Y
5 22 5 18 25   19 12 15 16 16 25

S P Y   H A V E ?
19 16 25   8 1 22 5

A   L I C E N S E
1   12 9 3 5 14 19 5

T O   S P I L L
20 15   19 16 9 12 12

Answers

Page 61

Ups and Downs

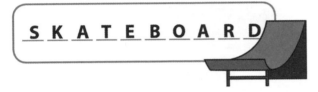

S K A T E B O A R D

Page 65

Expedition

EXPEDITION

deep	ion	pint
den	need	pit
dent	net	point
diet	next	pox
din	node	teen
dine	note	ten
dip	one	tend
done	oxen	tide
edit	pen	tie
edition	pent	tied
end	pet	tine
eon	pie	tip
exit	pin	ton
expend	pine	tone

Page 72

Werewolf Maze

Page 73

Wacky Wizards

Answers

Page 79
Types of Knots

Bowline	Figure eight	Loop	Reef knot	Slip knot
Coil	Half hitch	Overhand	Rope	Square knot

Page 80
Baseball Fever

Page 81
Helicopter Trip

HELICOPTER TRIP

cheep	hopper	propel
cheer	hotel	proper
chili	hotter	protect
chipper	otter	recipe
chirp	people	repel
citer	peril	reptile
clipper	piece	teeth
creep	piper	three
elite	pitch	treetop
erect	pitcher	tripe
ethic	poetic	triple
helper	police	tropic

Page 82
Rock and Roll

269

Answers

Page 84
Smart as a Whip

8	5	4	6	3	9	1	7	2
2	9	6	1	4	7	3	8	5
7	3	1	2	8	5	4	9	6
5	8	9	4	7	2	6	3	1
3	4	7	5	1	6	8	2	9
6	1	2	3	9	8	7	5	4
9	6	3	8	2	4	5	1	7
4	2	8	7	5	1	9	6	3
1	7	5	9	6	3	2	4	8

Page 85
Mixed-up Stories

1. After learning about coral reefs, Roberto asks his parents if he can take scuba diving lessons.

2. Roberto makes a scrapbook of pictures he took with a special under-water camera.

3. Roberto and his parents fly to the Bahamas to learn to scuba dive.

4. Roberto sees his favorite kind of fish, a parrot fish.

5. Roberto writes a report for science class and becomes interested in coral reefs.

6. Roberto and his parents get on a boat headed away from their hotel in the Bahamas.

5
1
3
6
4
2

Page 86
Explorer Maze

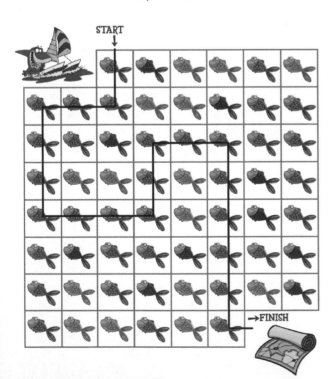

Page 87
Decode-a-Riddle

1=A	8=H	15=O	22=V
2=B	9=I	16=P	23=W
3=C	10=J	17=Q	24=X
4=D	11=K	18=R	25=Y
5=E	12=L	19=S	26=Z
6=F	13=M	20=T	21=U
7=G	14=N	21=U	

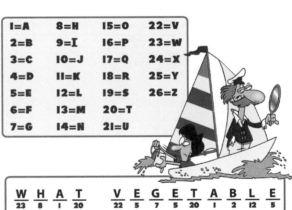

WHAT VEGETABLE
23 8 1 20   22 5 7 5 20 1 2 12 5

DO YOU NEVER
4 15   25 15 21   14 5 22 5 18

WANT TO BRING
23 1 14 20   20 15   2 18 9 14 7

ON A BOAT?
15 14   1   2 15 1 20

A LEAK
1   12 5 1 11

270

Answers

Page 90
Sports of all Sorts

Baseball   Football   Hockey   Softball   Tennis
Basketball   Golf   Soccer   Swimming   Volleyball

```
J B Q S S B F C H A S W L N
R V L U I C A L O O L Q S
K B L E B N M S F A A G I W
I N A R S X N T E B H H E I
O I B G J C E T U B M M
J F Y H P A U E T U A K E M
Y P E A L V K T R T F L B I
E I L L C S R E C C O S L N
K E L T A F O O T B A L L G
C B O R F Y K G Y N I A K Z
O M V L D O D I T I G X M D
H F O K F R T I W H D U Y D
Y G W O W C N M Q H O Y E M
V T C U W Z R N O M Q N F W
```

Page 93
No School Today!

Crossword solution:
- 1. SUMMER (across), SNOWSTORM (down from S)
- 2. HOLIDAY
- 3. SICK
- 4. CONFERENCE
- 5. MEETINGS

ACROSS
1. Season between Spring and Fall
2. Special type of "day" like Christmas or Easter
3. When you have a cold or toothache, you're ___SICK___.
4. When parents meet with teachers
5. Teachers go to these group events to discuss stuff.

DOWN
1. You do a lot of digging in these types of storms.

Page 98
Hockey Stuff

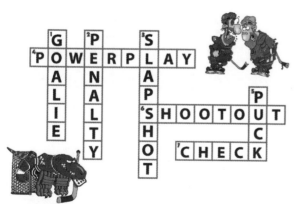

Crossword solution:
- 4. POWERPLAY
- 1. GOALIE (down)
- 2. PENALTY (down)
- 3. SLAPSHOT (down)
- 6. SHOOTOUT
- 5. PUCK (down)
- 7. CHECK

ACROSS
4. This happens when one team has more players on the ice than the other.
6. This is used to decide the winning team; players take turns trying to score.
7. To do this is to bump another player out of the way.

DOWN
1. This player tries to keep the other team from scoring.
2. A player gets this if he violates a rule.
3. A hard-hitting shot at the goal from a distance away
5. This is what all the players scramble to get.

Page 99
Super Strength

8	2	5	3	4	9	7	6	1
9	1	3	8	6	7	2	4	5
6	7	4	5	1	2	8	9	3
5	3	1	6	9	8	4	7	2
7	8	2	4	3	5	9	1	6
4	6	9	2	7	1	3	5	8
1	4	6	7	2	3	5	8	9
3	5	7	9	8	6	1	2	4
2	9	8	1	5	4	6	3	7

Answers

Page 102
Birthday Party

Page 103
Out of This World

Earth	Mars	Milky Way	Saturn	Venus
Jupiter	Mercury	Neptune	Uranus	

M N E B Y L M M S W O T G S
N I R W C O W E U F B V U S
A X L U S C X R N J H N Z J
X X I K T Y Y C A G E C U J
R A C U Y A N U R V O P M H
E A R T H W S R U I T R P
N Q H Y A Y A Y F T W L R K
E N U T P E N Y E X T X S P
J J J N O M I V R N E R V R B
A C D W Q D P O B X C O A B
Q K A C Y J U L B H R U M Q
R Y U L Z F V X U B U P G H
P W L U C X D U G T I Q I U
K L Z V M V Z M S T O N A Y

Page 104
Snow Day

Page 105
Out on the Lake

S A I L I N G

Answers

Page 110
Decode-a-Riddle

1=A	7=G	13=M	19=S	22=V
2=B	8=H	14=N	20=T	23=W
3=C	9=I	15=O	21=U	24=X
4=D	10=J	16=P		25=Y
5=E	11=K	17=Q		26=Z
6=F	12=L	18=R		

W H A T   D O   Y O U
23 8 1 20   4 15   25 15 21

D O   W I T H   A N
4 15   23 9 20 8   1 14

O L D   B I K E ?
15 12 4   2 9 11 5

Y O U
25 15 21

R E - C Y C L E I T
18 5 3 25 3 12 5 9 20

Page 111
Ice-Cream Truck

Page 112
Puppy Maze

Page 113
Globetrotter

GLOBE-TROTTER

bet	globe	reel
beet	goo	robe
beg	greet	robot
belt	leg	roe
better	let	role
blot	letter	root
bog	lob	rot
bolt	lobe	tee
boot	log	toe
bore	lore	tore
bottle	lot	tote
eel	oboe	treble
getter	otter	tree
glee	rebel	trot

Answers

Page 114
Go, Go, Go

Airplane	Car	Monster truck	Rickshaw	Wagon
Big rig	Helicopter	Motorcycle		Taxi	Yacht

```
E W G G V G P C V H B M J W
U N I D I U B C E H B O G A
S D A R K N F L C X M N J H
T O G L U T I A T H H S G S
P I H U P C M A Z E F T P K
B H C H O R Y A C H T E P C
D A U P W W I P Z D N R O I
R A T K R A Q A U Y T N R R
R E K K V N G Z P S N R X E
R E L C Y C R O T O M U C H
G M E B Y K U N N Z J C S T
I A C I L C A N H P L K T A
N Q P N N N F C Y M E C O X
S J A G Q E J M K N I R U I
```

Page 115
Car Parts

Crossword puzzle solution:
- 1. ENGINE (down)
- 2. TRUNK (across)
- 3. BRAKE (down)
- 4. MIRRORS (across)
- 5. SEATBELTS (down)
- 6. HORN (down)
- 7. RADIO (across)
- 8. AIRBAG (down)
- 9. TIRES (across)
- 10. HEADLIGHTS (across)

ACROSS
2. Storage space in back
4. Helps the driver see around the car
7. Plays music
9. The "shoes" of the car
10. Needed for driving at night

DOWN
1. The "heart" of the car
3. Makes the car stop
5. Keeps everyone in the car safe
6. Lets other drivers know where you are
8. Pops out if there's an accident

Page 116
Dinosaur Maze

Page 118
Golf

Ball	Club	Green	Par	Swing
Birdie	Course	Iron	Score	Wood

```
F R P X A E K O C P K G G
D F J C E L X W O W A P J
L S T E S W N R U N C R B
A K Z L L A B K R P A X G
I P L A N V J V S I M C C
F A Y E B Q W W E N T K O
V C E U N H W O F O I S S
D R L E B O Z L U J J O C
G C L W O I R O N B X O O
M F V D V R R B X G A R R
C O G C E M A D S E H N E
B C R P W X C B I P J G C
T J L S W I N G G E B H Y
```

Answers

Page 119
Cool Tree House

Page 123
Mixed-up Stories

1. Mark cooks some food in a special pot that hangs over his campfire.

2. Mark sets up his tent on the flattest spot.

3. Mark pours water over his campfire and stirs the ashes to make sure it is out.

4. Mark sweeps away any sticks and rocks so that his tent can lie flat.

5. Mark makes sure all his food is sealed up so animals don't bother him as he sleeps.

6. Mark gathers water to keep near his campfire, and small sticks to get the fire started.

__4__ __2__ __6__ __1__ __5__ __3__

Page 126
"B" There or "B" Square

Bahamas	Bangladesh	Belgium	Bolivia	Brazil
Bali	Barbados	Bermuda	Bosnia	Bulgaria

Page 127
Souvenirs

ACROSS
1. Dangles from a ring
3. Send this to a friend
5. Sticks to the fridge
6. Pull this over your head to show others where you've visited

DOWN
2. Goes on top of your head
3. Hang this on your wall
4. Be careful not to poke your finger with this!
5. Sip something from this

275

Answers

Page 129
Rebus Ruckus

"S A D D L E   U P"

Page 130
Perfect Skills

6	5	9	4	1	8	2	3	7
8	7	3	2	6	5	1	9	4
1	4	2	9	7	3	6	5	8
5	8	4	7	2	9	3	6	1
2	9	6	3	4	1	7	8	5
3	1	7	5	8	6	9	4	2
7	2	5	6	3	4	8	1	9
9	6	1	8	5	2	4	7	3
4	3	8	1	9	7	5	2	6

Page 134
All About Yo-Yos!

ACROSS
3. A move where your yo-yo "walks" on the ground; 3 words
4. A move where you start with the yo-yo on the ground; 2 words
5. A move where you let the yo-yo hang before flicking it back up; 2 words
6. A move where you flick the yo-yo down and let it hang and spin

DOWN
1. A move where you don't catch the yo-yo and let it fling around; 3 words
2. A move where you release the yo-yo behind you, then pull it forward; 2 words

Page 135
Ahoy, Matey!

Answers

Page 136
Darts Maze

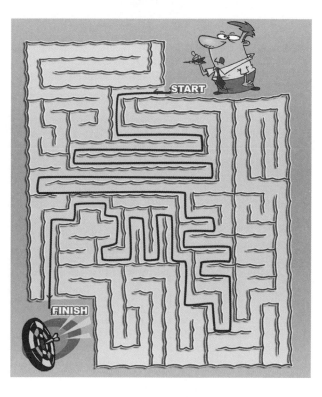

Page 137
Mixed-up Stories

1. A family listens to a tour guide talk about ancient ruins.

2. A family gets on a bus and takes their seats.

3. A family asks a tour guide to take their picture so they can always remember their trip.

4. A family wakes up in their hotel.

5. A tour guide asks if anyone has any questions.

6. A family arrives at the site of some famous ruins.

4 2 6 1 5 3

Page 139
Truckin' Around

Page 142
All-Star Hockey

Assist	Goalie	Overtime	Pass	Puck
Breakaway	Interference	Pad	Penalty	Rebound

```
B L O B I B N C M W M D S O
V P J E I X U C M K C U P P
E C N E R E F R E T N I L L
J P A S S Z W B U F E K G J
F H K G Z T P M Q Z P T R V
E Q A K Y A W A K A E R B E
K M A W D W B T D F B Q F Q
L Z I A R E B O U N D A L T
V B G T S N Y T L A N E P A
V R T O R S D C K A E W W Y
X R H Q A E I V S I C L J D
H I Z P F L V S X Q D D V Q
L A R M F N I O T D D J S Z
W B M F E L S E U P N F M H
```

Answers

Page 143
Fright Night

Page 148
Types of Spiders

ACROSS
4. Very poisonous; 2 words
5. Named for its sphere-shaped web; 2 words
6. ___WOLF___ spider; named after a fierce canine

DOWN
1. Named for the length of its limbs; 3 words
2. This type is sometimes a pet
3. Named for what it eats; 2 words (Hint: "It's a __BIRD SPIDER__, it's a plane!")

Page 151
Awesome Astronaut

Page 152
Zoo Crew

Alligator	Orangutan
Chimpanzee	Polar bear
Elephant	Rhinoceros
Giraffe	Tiger
Lion	Zebra

Answers

Page 153
Puzzle Power

4	1	3	6	7	8	2	5	9
6	8	2	9	3	5	7	4	1
7	5	9	4	2	1	6	3	8
3	9	4	5	1	6	8	2	7
1	7	5	8	9	2	4	6	3
8	2	6	3	4	7	9	1	5
9	3	7	1	6	4	5	8	2
5	6	1	2	8	9	3	7	4
2	4	8	7	5	3	1	9	6

Page 156
Blast Off Maze

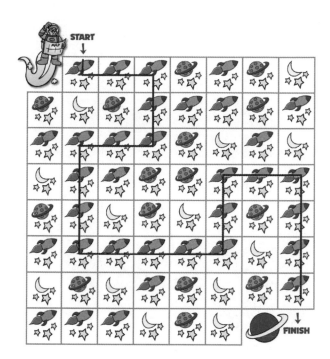

Page 157
Build It Up!

CONSTRUCTION

Page 160
Football Fun

Astroturf	End zone	Huddle	Playbook	Stadium
Blitz	Goalpost	Penalty	Quarterback	Touchdown

Answers

Page 162
Roller Coaster

Page 163
Under the Big Top

ACROSS
1. Also known as the "Big Top"
4. A really big animal
5. Elephants eats these

DOWN
1. Acrobats swing from these
2. These performers have colorful clothes and big noses.
3. People walk across this, if they can balance.

Page 164
Rocking Numbers

6	5	9	4	1	8	2	3	7
8	7	3	2	6	5	1	9	4
1	4	2	9	7	3	6	5	8
5	8	4	7	2	6	3	6	1
2	9	6	8	4	1	7	8	5
3	1	7	3	8	6	9	4	2
7	2	5	6	3	4	8	1	9
9	6	1	8	5	2	4	7	3
4	3	8	1	9	7	5	2	6

Page 166
Ready, Set, Go!

280

Answers

Page 167
Creepy Crawlers

```
¹A N ²T
    A
³S P I D E R
    A
    N        ⁴L
  ⁵C E N T I P E D E
    U          E
    L          C
  ⁶B U M B L E B E E H
    A
```

ACROSS
1. Digs a good picnic
3. Has eight legs
5. Has many, many legs
6. Has yellow and black stripes

DOWN
2. A hairy kind of spider
4. This type of worm sucks blood.

Page 180
Smart Math

1	8	4	6	3	5	7	2	9
6	2	3	7	8	9	1	5	4
9	5	7	2	1	4	8	3	6
3	4	1	8	9	2	6	7	5
7	9	2	3	5	6	4	1	8
8	6	5	1	4	7	2	9	3
4	1	6	5	7	3	9	8	2
5	7	9	4	2	8	3	6	1
2	3	8	9	6	1	5	4	7

Page 181
Let's Play!

M + 1 - E + (key) (bat) - T + (stairs/person) - STAI

M O N K E Y B A R S

Page 182
Pinewood Derby

PINEWOOD DERBY

bed	dewy	open
bind	died	own
binder	done	peer
bone	drop	pine
bored	dry	pony
bow	dye	red
brie	end	rib
brown	ewe	ripe
brownie	ion	robe
deep	nerd	weed
deer	nod	weep
deny	one	weird

Answers

Page 184
Cool Cowboy

Page 188
Parks and Recreation

Aquarium	Hiking trail	Ski slopes
Beach	Lodge	Summer camp
Campsite	Museum	Zoo
	Park	

```
A H L F K Z L K B Z S H R T
Q K O K D C I J R I S Z R B
U T D O F S A C C A U H W H
A J G A F H R M A C P D Q D
R A E U Y A N U M V Q P M P
I H K Z N T G I P S M O M B
U H C A E B N S S D I A B M
M M O F S A I E I M C T U P
P G E B W Z K X T R L S E N
S R O B V N I N E E E V R Y
O X C Y W W H M Z U S Z V A
O S S H Y B M F M I P U H K
Z M I Z Z U X Q L R V Z M D
Q S K I S L O P E S D V M A
```

Page 192
Water-Balloon Fight

WATER-BALLOON FIGHT

anthill	eight	large
antler	faint	light
ballet	father	organ
ballot	fellow	rainbow
bangle	fiber	robin
baring	fight	their
bellow	finger	tiger
bigfoot	float	tight
bitter	gorilla	tower
boating	grill	train
bottle	heart	tribe
eating	hollow	weight

Page 194
Straight Up!

4	2	8	5	3	7	1	6	9
7	5	3	9	1	6	2	4	8
1	6	9	4	8	2	5	3	7
9	1	4	3	6	5	8	7	2
6	7	5	8	2	9	3	1	4
3	8	2	1	7	4	6	9	5
2	3	7	6	9	8	4	5	1
5	9	1	2	4	3	7	8	6
8	4	6	7	5	1	9	2	3

Answers

Page 195
Water Park

Page 196
Pool Maze

Page 197
Masked Ball

Page 200
The Great Outdoors

Answers

Page 201
Summer Camp

ACROSS
4. Helps you cook things when you're out in the wilderness
5. You can float on the water in this
7. You might sleep in this
8. An adult who works at the camp

DOWN
1. You toast this over a campfire.
2. Tell this kind of story around a fire to spook the campers
3. Holds your water
6. Paddle this by yourself or with another person

Page 204
Types of Clothes

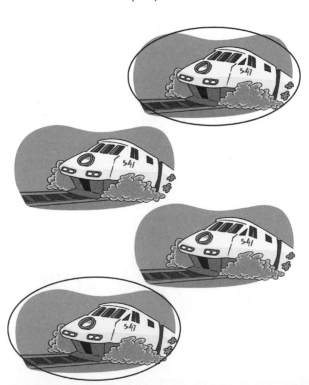

Page 208
Cat Maze

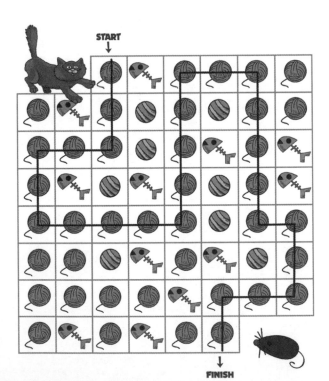

Page 209
Speedy Train

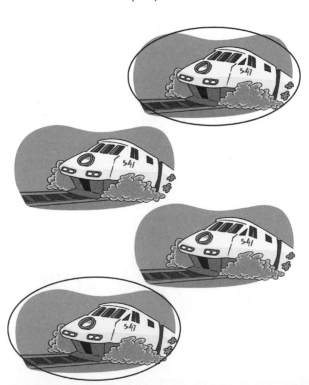

284

Answers

Page 212
Let's Party!

Balloons Cake Candy Friends Holiday
Birthday Candles Costume Gifts Sleepover

Page 213
What's Your IQ?

6	7	9	8	5	2	1	3	4
3	8	1	4	6	9	7	2	5
2	4	5	1	3	7	8	6	9
7	9	3	5	2	1	4	8	6
1	5	4	6	8	3	9	7	2
8	6	2	9	7	4	5	1	3
4	2	7	3	1	5	6	9	8
9	1	6	2	4	8	3	5	7
5	3	8	7	9	6	2	4	1

Page 217
Old West

Page 220
Shiver Me Timbers!

ACROSS
1. Pirates wear this on an eye
4. Another word for "my"
6. Sometimes pirates will give other pirates this type of "dot"
7. Weapon commonly used by pirates for defense
8. What pirates say when they see land
9. A pirate's main vehicle of transportation

DOWN
2. Means "yes"
3. This is shot out of a cannon
5. Some pirates have these in their ears

Answers

Page 224
Underwater Swimmer

S H A R K
A T T A C K

Page 225
Monster Maze

Page 226
Crime Fighter

Page 227
Camping

Backpack
Cabin
Campfire   Fishing   Sleeping bag   Tent
Campground   Ghost stories S'mores   Woods

Answers

Page 236
Wet Weather

R A I N C O A T

Page 238
Road Trip

Page 242
Decode-a-Riddle

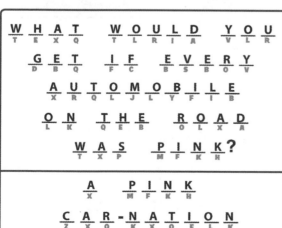

W	H	A	T		W	O	U	L	D		Y	O	U
T	E	X	Q		T	L	R	I	A		V	L	R

G	E	T		I	F		E	V	E	R	Y
D	B	Q		F	C		B	S	B	O	V

A	U	T	O	M	O	B	I	L	E
X	R	Q	L	J	L	Y	F	I	B

O	N		T	H	E		R	O	A	D
L	K		Q	E	B		O	L	X	A

W	A	S		P	I	N	K	?
T	X	P		M	F	K	H

A		P	I	N	K
X		M	F	K	H

C	A	R	-	N	A	T	I	O	N
Z	X	O		K	X	Q	F	L	K

Page 243
Into the Woods

Answers

Page 245
Super Solver

4	8	2	5	7	3	6	9	1
6	5	7	2	6	9	4	7	8
8	7	6	8	1	4	3	5	2
6	1	4	3	9	7	8	2	5
7	3	5	1	8	2	9	6	4
8	2	9	4	5	6	7	1	3
5	6	1	9	3	8	2	4	7
3	4	7	6	2	5	1	8	9
2	9	8	7	4	1	5	3	6

Page 247
Pool Party

Page 249
Winter Wonderland

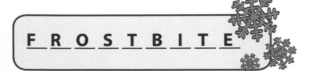

F R O S T B I T E

Page 251
School Maze

288